Tantric Pulsation

The journey of human energy from its animal roots to its spiritual flowering

By Aneesha L. Dillon

Tantric Pulsation

By

Aneesha L. Dillon

Copyright © 2005

ISBN 1-905399-01-4

Cover Design by Steve Foote
www.tinracer.com

Copyedited by Laurence Jones

PERFECT PUBLISHERS
23 Maitland Avenue
Cambridge
CB4 ITA
UK
www.perfectpublishers.co.uk

iv

Contents

Part One: Natural Health vs. Emotional Damage

1	Assessing the Damage	3
2	The Breathing Pulsation	15
3	The Orgasm Formula	27
4	Armoring: The Seven Segments	41
5	The Feeling Pairs	55

Part Two: Taking off the Armor

6	Preparing the Body	73
7	Unmasking the Face: Eyes	87
8	Unmasking the Face: Mouth & Throat	101
9	Freeing the Armored Heart	115
10	Through the Trapdoor	129
11	Into the Depths	141
12	Down to the Roots	155

Part Three: The Map of Pleasure

13.	The Tantra Experience	173
14.	The Tantric Milieu	187
15.	Exploring the Chakras	201
16.	The Circle of Light	215
17.	The Tantric Lifestyle	229

Introduction

I always felt my work to be a kind of calling, something I was born to do. A long time ago, while giving a session at the Esalen Institute in California, I was suddenly flooded with the feeling that what I was doing, in that moment, was exactly what I was meant to be doing for my life's work.

It was an ecstatic feeling, deeply satisfying, nourishing and fulfilling. This feeling hasn't changed; it has always been with me in relation to the Pulsation work.

A few years later, when I met Osho and recognized him as my spiritual Master, this underlying feeling about my work deepened and strengthened.

In this book, I hope to present what I have learned about human energy – the experiential understanding that I've gained in working with Reich's theories about the body and emotions.

Through actively participating for almost thirty years in Osho's vision of therapy and meditation, I have integrated the dimension of Tantra with these basic Reichian techniques.

My exploration continues. More and more, the Tantric dimension of my work is melded with the basic dynamics of emotional release and energizing the body.

For me, there is no full stop. It's a continuing process of growth and exploration.

If this book inspires you to explore your own life energy, discovering new levels of aliveness and ecstasy, then it will fulfill its purpose.

Acknowledgments

I tried for years to write this book myself and never seemed to have the time or space for it, due to my busy schedule of groups and trainings in Europe, India and elsewhere.

My old friend Subhuti – with whom I have shared many extraordinary creative projects, including four musical shows, in recent years – eventually persuaded me that by the time I was ready to sit down and start he would have it finished and in my hand.

So we embarked on a daily series of interviews, in which I poured out my understanding and experience. Sure enough, the book arrived in my hands, as promised.

I thank him from the bottom of my heart for his efficiency, humor and ability to cajole and harass me.

I also want to thank all the people who came to my groups over the years, who were my greatest teachers. What they opened and revealed in an atmosphere of trust and love helped to transform my life as well as theirs.

I wish to express my gratitude to Charles and Erica Kelley, my Reichian teachers, who gave me the tools for the outer work, and an even deeper gratitude to Osho, my spiritual Master, who gave me the tools for the inner work.

Osho's words have nourished my spirit for thirty years, his silence has touched my very core, and the dancing energy of his global buddhafield continues to sustain my journey.

For further information about Osho, his vision and his meditations, check the internet at www.osho.com

PART ONE

Natural Health

vs.

Emotional Damage

Chapter One

Assessing the Damage

I am a reluctant revolutionary. My work sets me against the conventions and morality of mainstream society because it shows me the damage that society does to ordinary people.

But I am not the type to stand on a soap box and wage a crusade. I have no great passion for overturning the status quo.

I simply see what reflects itself to me as I gently dig my fingers into the muscles of the people who come to me as clients. In this reflection, I see both the damage and the healing, the sickness and the cure.

For the past thirty years I have been a practicing Neo-Reichian therapist, applying basic principles discovered by Wilhelm Reich, a pioneering scientist and psychotherapist who lived in the first half of the twentieth century.

Practically, this means I use Reich's breathing and movement exercises to build up an intense charge of energy in the body of a client, which in turn creates an equally intense discharge of feelings and emotion.

In a way, the work I do is impersonal, because when you apply these principles almost everyone goes through the same process: building up energy, expressing and releasing feelings.

In another way, however, it is deeply personal, because what comes out with the feelings – assisted by my 'hands on' approach of prodding and massaging the body – is all the evidence of wrongdoing that each person has suffered.

And I am not a neutral observer. I can't stand aloof from this process as it unfolds before my eyes. With each client, I am intimately involved, experiencing the pain as he, or she, connects with long-forgotten emotional wounds and pent-up feelings, and experiencing the relief, lightness and joy when these things are released.

I'm not your traditional psychoanalyst, sitting safely on a chair behind the couch while the patient talks to the air. I'm right there, on the mat, guiding the client into a minefield of stored-up tension and memories, looking for the one that is ready to explode and poking it until it does.

And what comes out in this explosion, without exception, is an indictment of the way we are brought up, the way we are taught to live our lives.

So you see, I cannot help being a revolutionary, because it is my job to get rid of chronic problems caused by wrong upbringing and give people the chance to experience what it is like to be free, healthy, rebellious individuals.

Since the quality of rebelliousness seems to be an integral part of being an individual, revolution comes with the territory.

When people come to me, however, the deeper implications of what they are experiencing are usually hidden from view. It's the surface symptoms that prompt them to work with me.

Often, people realize the need for this kind of work when they start feeling miserable, or when their lives seem to be stuck in some kind of holding pattern, going neither higher nor lower but locked in monotony and routine.

They also come when emotions start to get out of control and they aren't sure why this is happening.

They come when they don't seem to be able to feel anything any more, whereas they can remember – years earlier – that life seemed brighter, fresher and more interesting.

In many, there is a sense that the fire of life has cooled to a lukewarm temperature and the flame is flickering and dim. Everyday life is being conducted at the minimum rather than the maximum.

They come, too, because they've invested a great deal of time and energy in reaching for the glittering prizes of success, only to realize that, somewhere along the way, they sacrificed real happiness and peace of mind for things that don't actually make them happy.

They come because they feel depressed, disturbed, angry or sad.

They come for many, many reasons but usually it has to do with some uncomfortable or painful feeling – "I don't like this and I want to get out of it."

Suddenly, it feels right to look for some kind of help, some roadmap for a new direction. That's when they come to an individual session with me, or to one of my groups or workshops.

Before explaining what I do in my sessions and groups, I'd like to look at some public examples, familiar to us all, of how damage happens to individuals.

For example, I've always had a soft spot in my heart for Prince Charles, the heir to the British throne. Maybe because we are the same age – fifty-four at the time of writing – and even though I am an American and he, of course, is English, I always had the sense that we grew up together.

Ever since I was a teenager, maybe even earlier, I was checking the papers and magazines to find out what he was doing. I really liked him and, in a long distance kind of way, identified with him.

Charles had to be 'a good boy' and I felt sorry for him, because he obviously couldn't scuffle around and get dirty, or, as soon as he did, he had to change his clothes. He couldn't run up and down the street, playing tag, hide and seek, kicking balls and climbing over other people's garden walls.

He had to be constantly controlling his behavior because somebody was always watching him. He couldn't even take a walk by himself. He always had somebody by his side to guard him, correct him, make sure he behaved as a good boy should – as an extraordinary boy should – and the miracle was that somehow he seemed to manage it.

One heard about certain eccentricities, such as talking to plants, experiments with ouija boards, interest in the occult, but

5

for a long, long time, first as a child and then as a man, Charles seemed able to toe the royal line.

Years later, I met Charles' cousin, Prince Welf of Hannover, and understood the crushing self-discipline demanded by this kind of public role. Welf told me, "This was the main thing that was drilled into my mind, again and again, as I grew up: 'Be careful what you do, people are watching you.'"

Welf was the great-grandson of the last German emperor and, like most European aristocracy, had no throne to sit on. But Charles did, making his behavior even more restricted.

What is the basic function of a royal? Have you ever thought about it?

As I see it, they act as role models for society. When all power was taken away from the monarchy, back in the days of Queen Victoria, the only function left for British royals was to act as supreme examples of how the common people should behave.

This role continues today. They are people to look up to, admire, imitate, identify with – just as I, in my own American way, identified with Charles.

Naturally, in such exposed roles, they have to behave as perfectly as they can and, generally speaking, Charles managed well until his fateful wedding with Diana Spencer.

That, too, began well, even magically. On their wedding day, it seemed to me that the entire British nation went into a collective orgasmic swoon when Charles kissed his young bride on the balcony of Buck House. At such a moment, you could almost hear the commentators announcing a fairytale ending: "…and they lived happily ever after."

But then, as everybody knows, the whole pack of royal playing cards came tumbling down, with revelation upon revelation: his mistress, her unhappiness, his withdrawal, her lovers, the secretly recorded conversations, the tabloid exposure, the paparazzi photographs….

And with Diana's first biography, penned by a close girlfriend under her own guidance, the sham of public pretense collapsed along with any hope of repairing the marriage.

6

What really happened to Charles? To me, he seemed torn apart by a deep conflict between his inclinations as a sensitive human being and his duties as a public icon. Or, more accurately, a conflict that had tortured him from the very beginning suddenly spilled out into the public eye, for all to see.

As he himself admitted, Charles never loved Diana. He married her because his father, Prince Philip, pressured him to do so, and because he was under a strong obligation to continue the royal bloodline and produce an heir. He chose duty over his personal feelings and created a nightmare.

And this, in a less dramatic way, is what happens to us all, from childhood onwards. This is how we are damaged and crippled, and this is why people come to me – to somehow heal themselves from this basic split between nature and society.

It doesn't have to be this way. We don't arrive here, on this planet, in a split condition.

The new-born child is one organic, harmonious, free-flowing fountain of energy – by energy I mean the life force that bubbles up from some mysterious source within us.

In traditional Chinese medicine this energy is known as 'chi;' in the ancient science of Indian yoga it is called 'prana,' and both systems describe it as existing both within the human body and floating freely in space.

In Western culture, Franz Mesmer called it 'animal magnetism,' Charles von Reichenbach called it 'odyle,' Henri Bergson the élan vital, the 'vital force.' To Sigmund Freud it was 'libido' and to Wilhelm Reich 'orgone.'

In the young child, this energy is undivided and uncontrolled. It expresses itself spontaneously through all kinds of natural impulses and uncivilized behavior.

The child knows nothing of manners. When unhappy, it cries loudly. When delighted, it laughs. It runs around when active and immediately lies down and sleeps when tired. It sucks at the breast without saying 'may I?' or 'thank you,' and pushes food away without saying 'sorry, I'm full.' It burps, farts, pees and takes a dump without even thinking of social etiquette.

7

But slowly, a process of training and education starts to shape the child's energy and behavior – for the two go very much together.

Much of this training is necessary. The child has to be trained to use a potty, to wear clothes, to avoid dangers like playing with boiling water on the kitchen stove or running out into the street without looking...

In a thousand different ways, the caring parents have to train the child so that it can learn to take care of itself and function in this world.

This educational process affects the free-flowing energy. It begins to take a certain shape, expressing itself according to social requirements: this is the time and place to eat... this is the time and place to run around and shout and scream and play... this is the time to sleep.

Parallel to this process, damage to the child's energy system starts to occur. Some of this damage is inevitable – just part of the knocks and scrapes that all growing things encounter.

For example, why does a tree end up with a kink or twist in its trunk? Maybe, accidentally, it got kicked when it was small, or knocked by a car. Then the tree grows crooked.

It's a condition of life. Sometimes growing is painful, sometimes easy and graceful, and there is no one really to blame.

For instance, when a child is sick and has to go to hospital, perhaps its mother and father cannot stay twenty-four hours in the ward. They have work to do, money to earn, other children to care for, and maybe the hospital rules prohibit sleeping over.

Often, in such a situation, the child will feel abandoned, rejected and later on may be angry with the parents, blaming them: "How could you do that to me? I'm your child! You don't love me!"

For the child, this makes sense, because abandonment was an undeniable emotional experience. For the parents, it was a totally different reality:

"But we had to do it, sweetheart," they explain patiently. "You were sick and needed an operation, otherwise you may have died."

In this way, parents act with the best of intentions, but emotional wounding happens in spite of it. Even if the child's conclusion is wrong, it can be wounded by its own misunderstanding – by not being able to digest or accept something that to the parents is obviously the right thing to do.

This is what I call 'unavoidable' or 'inevitable' damage to an individual's energy system. In most cases it is not serious and can be easily healed.

In addition, however, there is an enormous amount of unnecessary damage caused by the social conditioning process.

Every child is given a set of ideals by the parents – how they would like that child to be. And the problem is that these ideals do not necessarily, or maybe ever, support the natural expression of the child's energy and individuality.

So the child is trained, or conditioned, to act against its own nature, and this creates a basic split. It seems to happen to every human being.

The two areas where conditioning is most harmful are emotions and sexuality. It is here that the deepest damage occurs:

"Don't laugh... Don't cry... Don't be angry... Don't be sad...."

Most of us can remember occasions when, while growing up, our emotions were choked back, when we had to swallow our tears, our rage, when we had to hide our feelings and pretend to be something we were not.

We were told to smile when we wanted to shout and scream. We were told to make polite conversation when we wanted to weep. All this had a direct and powerfully negative impact on our energy, crippling its expression.

In the same way, sex energy was repressed, driven down into the dark, hidden from public view, as if it did not exist: "Don't touch yourself there... Don't have sexual thoughts... Sex is dirty... Don't masturbate or you'll go blind....'' This, too, impacted our energy, strangling it at the very source.

It may be argued that this kind of training and conditioning is as necessary as the other forms I have described. Indeed, many people are convinced this is so, arguing that the natural, animal impulses of the child have to be strictly tamed and channeled into civilized behavior.

But the truth is that the cure is worse than the imagined disease, the solution more damaging than the problem.

It was Sigmund Freud and one of his brightest disciples, Wilhelm Reich, who discovered that sexual repression lies at the root of psychological neurosis. And it was Reich who went on to discover that the deadness and stiffness from which all adults suffer is caused directly by sexual and emotional repression.

I agree absolutely with Reich. My own personal experience in working with thousands of people makes it irrefutable. By stuffing down the energy that seeks expression through sex and feelings, especially when young, we are effectively killing ourselves, making ourselves incapable of enjoying life.

Seeing the situation, Reich plunged into a long battle with the European and American cultures in which he lived and worked, challenging their basic attitudes and assumptions.

He advocated sexual freedom for all human beings from birth and infancy onwards. By this he meant the growing child should feel supported in its natural biological drive, should be able to suck at the breast, have close physical contact with the mother and be able to play with its own genitals.

Girls and boys should be allowed to enjoy the 'sexual play' phase that spans the ages five through seven, and, after puberty, sexual freedom for teenagers is seen as both natural and important in maintaining a healthy psyche.

Reich wrote books, opened clinics, made speeches – not only on the theme of sexual freedom, but on a wide range of related issues, including the importance of emotional expression and the benefits of 'orgone' therapy. He also pointed out the social cost of repression, including sexual perversion, pornography,

10

prostitution, domestic violence, rape, depression and all kinds of psychological problems.

Needless to say, he attracted opposition wherever he went – in Austria, Germany, Denmark, Norway and the United States – and in 1957 died of a heart attack in an American jail at the age of sixty. To me, he was one of the most controversial and misunderstood men of the twentieth century.

Reich left behind him, however, a treasure trove of discoveries, including a practical method, or process, for removing the energy blocks in the human body caused by sexual and emotional repression, and restoring an individual's vitality and zest for life.

It is with these tools that I do my work. I learned them from an American Neo-Reichian teacher and scientist, Charles Kelley, who studied and worked personally with Reich, and who founded the Radix Institute in California, where I did my training.

As I said in the beginning, I am no public crusader. I have no desire to challenge the moral attitudes of society and fight with them. I simply enjoy helping people rediscover their natural love of life, their feelings of joy and happiness, their basic 'yes' to living, which to me comprise the essential part of human experience.

At the same time, I do see changes happening at the social level that I find encouraging. As in the case of Prince Charles, the role models that are offered as examples of how we should live – or, more accurately, how we should die and still appear to be alive – cannot stand the close scrutiny of the modern media and instant transmission of information.

We are seeing behind the façade. And here I must applaud Charles for his honesty and sincerity, the way he admitted his faults, publicly acknowledging his failure as Diana's husband and his love for his mistress, Camilla Parker Bowles. Such candidness from a Royal icon, such evidence of human frailty, is an encouraging sign.

Similarly, in my own country, the political scandal involving President Bill Clinton and Monica Lewinsky was significant in

11

that, when their secret affair was suddenly exposed to public scrutiny by investigator Ken Starr, almost the entire media and political establishment called for the president's resignation.

But Clinton refused to go and the public supported him. The ordinary voters knew he had been set up by a bunch of hypocrites – people who preached morality in public but behaved very differently in private – and they forgave their president. That is the reason he was able to stay in power. Even today, when he is no longer in office, thousands of people flock to hear Clinton speak – they still adore him.

Meanwhile, the widespread revelations around the world of how so-called 'celibate' Catholic priests are involved in of all kinds of sexual perversions, including pedophilia, has demonstrated the absolute futility of fighting with our basic nature.

We are sexual beings and sex energy is the source of all growth, intelligence and creativity. Celibacy is not only difficult, it is immensely destructive and biologically impossible – and it will be a great day for human progress when the Vatican acknowledges this simple fact.

These are all welcome cracks in the collective façade, evidence of how human nature must inevitably come into conflict with social attitudes that are rooted in ignorance and outdated attitudes.

The irony is that, most of the time, we don't even remember why or how these attitudes were formed. We just pass them on, unthinkingly, from generation to generation, compelled by a tribal-based desire to fit in, to follow the norm, and by the deep-rooted fear of being branded social outcasts if we do not.

For example, staying a virgin until marriage is still prized among certain sections of the American public – in the 1990's more than 2.5 million teenagers between 16 and 18 years took a 'virginity pledge' propagated by various religious organizations.

But the origins of virginity have nothing to do with purity or morality. Anthropologists have established beyond all doubt that virginity became important in social development with the introduction of private property, in male chauvinist cultures, so

12

the man could ensure that his children and heirs came from his own semen, his own bloodline.

It was only later that religion sanctified the practice and turned it into something holy, thereby reinforcing the grip of a male-dominated society. And, of course, in every age and in every culture, it has been 'okay' for young men to 'fuck around' and 'sow their wild oats.' It is only the women who must remain chaste.

However, interesting though these cultural phenomena are, this is not my work or my passion. I am no more an historian of social injustice to women than I am a political revolutionary.

Back in the early Seventies, when I was living in San Francisco, feeling the first exciting possibilities of sexual freedom and getting out of the grip of a Fifties-style morality, I certainly had the sense that I was part of a widespread sexual revolution.

With the introduction of the birth control pill, I was a member of the first generation of women in history to be in full control of our own bodies. It was up to me to decide whether or not I wanted to get pregnant, or whether my sexual energy and orgasms could be enjoyed simply as fun.

Incidentally, this was also the time when I connected with Reich, because reading his books I realized he was saying the same thing that I was experiencing. In fact, Reich's battles paved the way for the sexual revolution to happen.

In my enthusiasm and naivety, I thought this revolution would create a permanent change in public attitudes. Later on, I saw the pendulum swing the other way, back towards puritanism, and understood how transient such social moods can be.

Fortunately, my focus has always been on individual experience, not on collective movements. I'm not waiting for the Age of Aquarius to dawn on humanity before celebrating my own life. I do my work simply because I love it, not with any great expectation that it will change the world.

My job is to help people who have understood something very basic about their own conditioning, that they have been

13

damaged, to show them how this can be healed and to guide them through the process.

This is my work, my love affair with life, and this book is devoted to an explanation of my methods.

One more thing I would like to say at the outset: my work does not stop with Reich.

Prodigious and profound though his effort has been, to me it was, and is, incomplete. It strives to restore health and happiness to the human condition, but it lacks a spiritual dimension, which is a great pity because all the groundwork for such a dimension has been prepared.

Reich himself was against religion, but that was – I suspect – because he saw it only in terms of the established church, which to him was one of the primary causes of the damage to his clients.

As I see it, the spiritual path of Tantra can be embraced as a natural evolution of Reich's work, because it starts from the same point. It begins with the physical body, with sex energy, and reaches upward toward the mystical dimension of meditation.

As this book develops, I will be describing how this happens, how Reichian methods evolve into Tantra. I will also be introducing the work of another visionary, Osho Rajneesh, an Indian mystic who has given Tantra a context that is relevant to the twenty-first century and which goes far beyond the popular idea that it is just a way to enjoy better sex.

But first things first. I must begin with the most basic step in this process: the pulsation of breathing.

Chapter Two

The Breathing Pulsation

The word 'Pulsation,' which I've chosen to call my work, refers to the breathing pulsation, the 'in' and 'out' of the breath that begins with birth and ends with death. It is with us throughout our lives, whether we are aware of it or not, and is deeply connected with life at its very source.

To breathe is to live...taking air in...letting it out...it is so fundamental and basic to our daily existence that we almost never think about it. This constant swing between the polarities of taking in and letting out is the pulsation to which I'm referring.

There are many pulsations in the life of the body: the heartbeat, the blood vessels, the squeezing action of the intestines...everything is moving inside the body and it has a certain rhythm – a pulsating rhythm.

When somebody is sick, or lying unconscious, what is the first thing that a doctor checks? Of course, everybody knows: he takes hold of the wrist and feels the pulse. It is a quick way to assess the situation.

The doctor is inquiring, "Is this body pulsating in a healthy way, or is something seriously wrong?"

In ayurveda, the traditional Indian healing system, the pulse provides an encyclopedia of information about the rest of the body. A skilled practitioner can tell – just by feeling your pulse – the condition of your internal organs, the presence of tumors and other diseases, the state of your immune system and so on.

Chinese acupuncture functions in a similar way.

In my work, the significance of pulsation as an indication of human health stems directly from the discoveries of Wilhelm Reich, so it will be helpful to say something about his work.

Reich's understanding of pulsation grew out of his interest in medicine and psychology. Born in 1887 and growing up on a farm in the German Ukraine, he began to study medicine at the University of Vienna at the age of twenty one.

There, he quickly became interested in the revolutionary new science of psychoanalysis being developed by Professor Sigmund Freud, and after several personal meetings so impressed the older man that he was permitted to join the Vienna Psychoanalytic Association two years before he gained his medical degree. Until then, only certified doctors were admitted.

Reich's brilliance as an analyst and author of numerous important articles on psychoanalysis caused Freud to select him as his assistant physician when Freud opened a public clinic in Vienna in 1922.

Reich was impressed with Freud's libido theory, agreeing that sex shapes the human psyche. He also agreed that it is damage to the sexual impulse – incurred during childhood and early social education – that lies at the root of human neurosis.

But there was an important difference between the two men: Reich saw sex as an energy phenomenon rather than merely psychological. And it was his search for the roots of this energy that led him to spend long hours peering into microscopes as part of an in-depth study of biology – an indication of Reich's endless curiosity and wide-ranging thirst for knowledge that extended far beyond the human mind and body.

Specifically, Reich was studying the behavior of single cell creatures, like the amoeba, noting how they pulsate in a rhythmic pattern, and how this pulsating energy flows inside the enclosed space of the cell.

Reich observed that the striving of the energy to extend beyond the boundary of the cell usually results in a characteristic shape, rather like a kidney, which Reich described as a basic life form. Seeds, plant bulbs, animal reproductive

16

cells and embryos, organs of the body, single-cell organisms, the early human foetus, all fit this model.

Observing this basic shape in its simplest form, such as an amoeba, Reich could see how the plasma – the living liquid content of the organism – moves around inside the cell. The plasma moves, not in one continuous movement, but in rhythmic impulses...pulsations.

There is a movement outwards, followed by a withdrawing inwards; a striving towards something, and a retracting from it. In this fundamental biological pulse of life, Reich saw little difference between an amoeba reaching out towards a food particle and a pair of human arms reaching toward a beloved.

He saw that human expressions of feeling also follow the same basic pulse: anger pours out through the organism toward an object, while fear contracts and pulls away from it.

According to Reich, this movement functions in all of nature. Everything is pulsating, everything is moving in its cycles of expansion and contraction: a jellyfish slowly moving through the ocean, a flower opening and closing, a human being waking up and going to work, then coming home, relaxing and going to bed.

Both polarities of the pulsation are needed. For example, you can't have endless expansion; you can't just keep on working and working. You will get completely exhausted. You need the opposite polarity. You need to rest, come back to yourself, recharge your batteries.

Similarly, with the breathing pulsation, you can't just breathe in and in and in. You will simply burst. The exhale has to be allowed so that a healthy pulsation can happen.

As you can imagine, the ability of human beings to pulsate in this way is affected strongly by the environment in which we live, and especially by the people with whom we are living.

For example, a small child is playing in his room. His breathing pulsation is healthy and normal. His mom has just given him a set of paints and a big piece of white paper – placed carefully on a plastic sheet on the floor – so he can happily splash away and enjoy himself. But then, unexpectedly, she has to go out and, after a while, the child finds it much more entertaining to paint pictures on the wall of his bedroom.

His father, just now returning from work, spent the whole of last weekend putting a brand new coat of paint on this very wall. It cost him time and money. When he sees the mess, he is furious with his small son.

He yells. He stomps his foot. He snatches the paint box and throws it in the garbage can. Maybe he even hits the child.

What happens to the child's breathing pulsation?

It stops. For a moment, everything freezes: both the in-breath and out-breath. The pulsation is interrupted as the child goes into a state of shock, then resumes at a minimum level.

But then, of course, things move on: dad goes to take a shower, mom comes home, learns what has happened and immediately feels guilty because she should have taken more care. She takes the child in her arms and offers comfort. The child starts breathing normally again and begins to cry.

Supper that night, in this particular household, is not a cheerful affair. The child continues to cry and finally his father gets angry again – he really needed a quiet evening after a lousy day at the office – and says sternly, "Stop that! Don't cry!"

The child now has to hold back the tears, swallow down the feelings, and for this he needs to again diminish the breathing pulsation, because if he breathes then he starts to feel and if he feels he starts to cry – it's that simple.

In other words, breathing is intimately connected with the emotional, expressive life of the body, and also with energy. The child in this story is not just stuffing down tears and emotions. He is trying to suppress a strong energy that wants to be released.

As I mentioned in the previous chapter, Reich agreed with Chinese medicine and Indian yoga that we are not made solely of physical matter, of flesh, blood and bones. We are also energy beings.

There is a subtle, invisible aura that infuses and surrounds the physical body, called an 'energy body,' which is sustained by the breathing pulsation. When we breathe in, we don't just inhale oxygen. We take in energy from the surrounding atmosphere and this nourishes the energy body.

Yoga has developed a special way of breathing, usually referred to as 'prana breathing,' or 'pranayama,' that is designed to enhance the intake of energy as a way of charging the energy body.

The existence of this phenomenon called energy is hard to prove, because it is too subtle to be quantified or measured, but is easy to experience or observe.

If we again take the example of a small child, we can observe an almost inexhaustible potential for physical activity and recreation that is clearly driven by something beyond muscle power.

I have heard of an experiment in which a professional athlete was given the task of copying the antics of a small boy: running around, rolling over and over, jumping up and down... imitating anything and everything the child felt like doing.

Naturally, the child enjoyed this novel game and had a great time, inventing new ways to jump, skip and move until the athlete was completely exhausted – well before the boy was ready to give up playing.

Why? Because a small child is close to an unimpeded source of free-flowing energy, whereas in an adult this same source has been conditioned and confined.

Interesting though such experiments may be, my own understanding of energy is not built on the investigations of others but on my own work experience. I hope that, as I describe my work in the ensuing chapters, the function of energy in the human body will become clear.

Reich asserted that 'orgone' energy is free-floating, not only within the earth's atmosphere but in all of space. The more orgone we can take in and absorb, the more the energy body is charged with vitality.

Perhaps I should mention that in the world of esoteric science, the human organism has seven bodies, just as it has seven chakras, or energy centers, and I will go into more detail about them later in the book.

The energy body I am talking about is known as the 'second body,' because it is the one that stays closest to the physical body, extending two or three inches beyond the surface of the skin.

It is this 'second body' that connects to our emotions. It flows throughout our physical form and affects the plasma, the liquid contents of the body – not difficult, because we are at least seventy percent water – and this in turn creates our feelings and emotions.

Think of it as a breeze blowing through our whole organism, causing ripples on our inner lake that stir emotions hidden beneath the surface. This is a poetic view. If you require a more detailed bio-chemical and bio-electrical explanation of how this works, I must refer you to Reich's prolific writings on the subject.

For the moment, it is enough to know that our emotions are governed by inter-action between the physical body and the energy body, with the breathing pulsation as an important link.

Pulsation in any living organism is a movement between the two polarities of core and periphery. In an amoeba, for example, the act of reaching out for a food particle is a movement from the core to the periphery. Taking in the particle, digesting and absorbing it, is a movement in the other direction, from the periphery to the core.

It's the same with human beings. The breath symbolizes – even embodies in a literal sense – the twin polarities of contact between ourselves and the outside world.

To the extent that we can fully take a breath in, we allow the outside world to enter inside and let it meet with our core, with our center. Here, 'core' is not so much a precise physical location as an energetic center, approximately corresponding to our guts, or belly.

Similarly, to the extent that we can fully breathe out, allowing the outward movement of our energy, we can move from our center to the periphery to meet the outside world.

In the world of Tantric sexuality, two people can meet, melt and merge only to the degree that they can move deeply into this pulsating movement between periphery and core. When you really breathe in, you receive your lover into the core of yourself. When you breathe out, you flow towards your beloved. In this way, two lovers create a kind of pulsating sexual dance which becomes orgasmic as the two organisms merge energetically through the second body into one.

More subtle dimensions are also involved in Tantra, including the upper chakras, giving an experience of oneness not only with the beloved but with existence itself. At root, however, it is the physical body and energy body, ignited by the breathing pulsation, which create the foundation of Tantric love making.

This may be a good moment to ask yourself a few questions:

Do I really allow life in? Do I really welcome what life is giving me – the whole spectrum of experience?

If not, then your in-breath is likely to be relatively shallow. It will not be as deep and total as it could be. It will be carefully controlled, symbolizing a cautious approach to life.

You can also ask:

Do I give myself to others and to the world surrounding me? Do I generously share my energy and participate fully in the dance of life?

If not, then your out-breath will also be restricted, staying within its full potential. In other words, the health and vitality of our breathing pulsation directly reflects our attitude to the world, and vice versa.

This is an appropriate moment to introduce a basic concept that I use in my work, which is the visualization of a hollow tube inside the body, beginning at the mouth and going all the way down to the lower belly. Through using this tube, we gain a better understanding of the breathing pulsation.

Partly, this tube is a physical reality, corresponding to our anatomy: a bronchial tube extends from the mouth down the throat and, dividing itself into ever-smaller passages, penetrates into the lungs as far down as the diaphragm.

21

Another tube, the esophagus, passes from the throat down into the stomach, but this is for food and drink, not for air.

However, when I ask people to close their eyes and take a deep inhale, they can easily have the impression that they are taking in air all the way down to the belly.

Why? Because when we breathe in deeply, the diaphragm – a thin but strong sheet of muscles at the bottom of the rib cage – flexes downwards and pushes the stomach muscles outwards, giving us the feeling that air is moving into the belly.

As we breathe out, the diaphragm relaxes and rises upwards, so the belly falls inwards again, and this gives us the sensation that air is moving up from the stomach to the chest and throat, on its way to being expelled through the mouth.

At an energy level, this hollow tube really exists. When the diaphragm drops down and pulls air into the bottom of the lungs, a flow of energy riding on the in-breath continues down into the belly.

Many people don't breathe this deeply, so the diaphragm remains frozen, keeping the energy flow confined to the upper part of the body. When I ask people to visualize a hollow tube and begin breathing into the belly, this gives mobility to the diaphragm for the first time in a long while, allowing a charge of vitality to enter the lower part of the body.

Usually, at the beginning of my groups, I introduce the idea of a hollow tube and have people breathe in the way I have just described, so they can feel how it functions as a channel for energy. This will be one of their basic tools in the work ahead.

Then I talk about pulsation, the movement between core and periphery, and guide participants through a series of simple exercises that give them a taste of it.

For example, I ask people to stand in a relaxed way, eyes closed, placing both hands on the lower belly. In order to feel this area more fully, I sometimes suggest that they make hip circles, since this creates a sensation of a still point, core, or center, in the middle of a rotating pelvis.

Then, with eyes open, I invite them to begin walking around the room, hands on the belly, keeping in touch with this center while taking note of their surroundings. I also remind them to be aware of their breathing, especially in the inhale, since each in-breath can be a reminder of staying inside oneself.

After a while, I ask people to let their attention shift to the periphery by walking faster and letting go of the belly so they can swing their arms, becoming conscious of the fact that arms and hands, legs and feet all exist at the periphery of the body.

The eyes, too, are at the periphery – they are our main gateway to the world – so I invite people to forget the belly and be more present in the eyes.

"You are coming alive on the outside of your body," I suggest. "Start to run a little bit, start to meet other people with your eyes, maybe touch hands as you pass, briefly say hello, become more light, more peripheral, moving and running… let your attention be all on the outside."

A kind of party game atmosphere soon builds up in the room as people run in and out of a moving crowd, touching hands, weaving and dodging, shouting 'hi' and 'bye' and other quick greetings to each other.

Gradually, I slow the pace down again and invite people to notice how easy it is to forget one's own center when so much activity is happening on the periphery.

"So now, as you walk, let yourself again make contact with your belly, with your own center, letting your movements slow down, so that, when you breathe in, you have the sense that your breath again touches down into your core.

"Let your walk become slower. Finally, come to a stop, to a place where you are still and silent."

In this way, I help people practice shifting their attention from the core to the periphery and back again, repeating the process several times to underscore the point.

"It's a very natural pulsation," I explain. "Sometimes you are 'outside,' in contact with the world, sometimes you are 'inside,' more in contact with yourself."

Often, I gather people in one big circle, holding hands together, and ask them to breathe deeply in through the mouth while lifting their arms high over their heads, leaning back and feeling the breath going right to the core. Then, letting the hands drop down and bending the body forwards, breathing fully out, making the sound 'Hah!'

We start out slowly and speed up until we are going really fast: "Ha! Ha! Ha!" It is an emphatic and vigorous demonstration of the two-part breathing pulsation.

In the next stage, I ask everyone to stand separately, one foot forward and one foot back, hands and arms stretched out in front of them at the level of the upper chest.

"When you breathe in, let your weight shift to your back foot and lean back, bringing your hands towards your mouth, as if you're taking in air with your hands. Then, still inhaling, turn your hands palms downwards and bring them down the front of your body, as if you are pushing the air down inside you, all the way into your belly," I explain.

"When you breathe out, shift your weight onto your front foot and lean forward, letting your hands come up the body and stretch out in front of you, in a kind of giving gesture, as if pushing the air out again."

I also suggest that people close their eyes when they breathe in, helping to create the sensation of remaining at home in one's own center, or core, and then opening the eyes when breathing out, to help the movement toward the periphery.

When guiding people through this part of the exercise, I sometimes emphasize the out-breath, making it forceful and explosive, while keeping the in-breath soft and slow, then reverse the pattern with a sharp in-breath and a slow, gentle out-breath.

In the final stage, I ask people to find a partner and explore the breathing pulsation together in a playful and creative way.

"See if you can discover your own pulsation movement, with the two of you breathing in and out together," I suggest. "It can be any movement, just find a way to breathe and move together in harmony."

People swing their arms from side to side, or up and down, bending this way and that, making arm circles and other gestures. It's a way of experiencing that pulsation can take a myriad of forms – it's not restricted to a fixed format – and also a fun way for people to connect at the beginning of a workshop. This partner exercise can be expanded to include four, then eight, then sixteen and even thirty-two people, spontaneously creating ever-larger and more complex organisms which nonetheless soon manage to discover a common pulsation.

With all of these exercises, I tend to follow a certain energetic pattern, starting slowly, letting people become familiar with the movements and breathing, then quickening the pace, building up speed and intensity to a crescendo. Then I let the energy subside again, with breathing and movement slowing and softening.

It's a form of pulsation in itself.

When people have gained some practical experience of pulsation, I make a simple diagram illustrating how energy flows in the human organism. This consists of a large circle representing the periphery and a small circle in its middle, representing the core.

I explain the dynamic movement between the two polarities, with the in-breath penetrating from periphery to core, the out-breath moving from core to periphery. I emphasize the importance of understanding this basic dynamic as we go deeper into Reich's process of re-awakening to the life force.

I also mention his ideas about orgone as energy that is free-floating in space and also permeates the human body.

"We cannot measure orgone through scientific instruments but you can experience it yourselves during this workshop," I explain.

"Reich talked about it as being everywhere. If you look out into a clear blue sky on a bright sunny day, you can sometimes see little squiggles in the air. On a dark murky day, you don't notice them much, but on a clear day you see them quite easily.

"This phenomenon, according to Reich, is free-floating energy. When you were a child, if you talked about it, your mother probably said, 'It's in your eyes, dear.' But Reich would disagree, saying this is free-floating orgone, which we can absorb in greater quantities if we breathe more deeply."

To make my own position clear, I explain that I am not an unconditional believer in Reich. My emphasis is not on his theories, but on the effects of his work. Whether he is right or not, the exercises and processes developed on the basis of his discoveries work like a charm. To me, that's what matters.

I am not a scientist or theoretician. I am in the resurrection business. I help people who have been half-dead to come alive. In this enjoyable and fulfilling work, I owe a huge debt to Reich – and his disciples, particularly Charles Kelley – for showing me the practical steps needed to restore human vitality to its natural, healthy state.

When I explore the implications of pulsation, when I see its effects on people, it brings to me the sense of wonder that underlies my work. On a practical level, I work with emotional release and freeing suppressed energies, but the effect goes much deeper than one can imagine.

It can take people to a place inside themselves where they experience a sense of oneness with the universe.

This understanding is not intellectual but *organismic*.

Experiencing the wholeness of their own body, they experience the wholeness of life itself. Feeling the body pulsating naturally, they feel in harmony with the pulsation of the cosmos.

This brings tremendous peace, acceptance and relaxation.

As the mystics say, to be in contact with your self puts you in contact with the larger 'Self' – the Self of all of life. When you go deep into the source of your own energy, you come to the source of all.

Chapter Three

The Orgasm Formula

You don't need to know a formula in order to have an orgasm. You don't even need to know the word 'orgasm.' If you are in tune with your own sexual energy, and if you are willing and able to allow this energy to express itself in a natural way, orgasm happens by itself.

But, whether we are aware of it or not, the process of having a sexual orgasm follows a certain formula, involving a build up of energy and excitement within the body, reaching towards climax and release. All kinds of muscles and nerves are involved, blood rushes to the sexual organs, bio-electrical currents sparkle and sizzle, faces flush, skin tingles... one way or another, the whole organism of the human body gets involved.

Moreover, this formula has implications that extend far beyond sexual enjoyment, because the same principles apply to emotional expression. Understanding the orgasm formula and applying its principles to the area of human feelings provides a key to helping people release blocked emotions, restore energy flow throughout the body and regain emotional health.

In other words, the orgasm formula creates a solid base for my work. That's why I have devoted this chapter to an explanation.

It was Reich who first dared to study the phenomenon of orgasm, breaking major social taboos in his efforts to understand the roots of human sexual energy, its effect on our psyche and on our ability to lead happy, fulfilling lives.

27

Reich's interest in sex wasn't just academic. It was deeply personal. From an early age he was fascinated with sex and, having observed two of his family's servants engaging in sexual intercourse, he attempted to make love with his brother's nurse at the age of four. At the age of eleven, he was making love with the family's cook, and at fifteen he was regularly visiting a brothel.

Sex remained very important to Reich during his whole life. He needed to make love every day, but he was not a playboy. Rather, he practiced what I would call 'serial monogamy' – enjoying a series of intense love relationships, one after the other, that were more or less monogamous.

The rest of his immense vitality he poured into his work. In fact, one can say that work and sex meant everything to him, and were always somehow connected in his approach to life. "Love, work and knowledge are the wellsprings of our life. They should also govern it" – that's the opening statement he makes in the introduction to many of his books.

Reich's interest in the function of orgasm arose out of his work as an analyst in Freud's Vienna clinic in the early 1920's. When he examined the lifestyles of patients who were successfully cured of psychological neurosis and compared them with those who could not be cured, he found that cured patients were able to enjoy a satisfactory sexual life, while the others could not.

The next step was obvious: in order to cure a patient of neurosis, sex energy had to be released from any inhibitions. But the sex act, in itself, did not guarantee a cure. It was not enough for a man or woman to make love frequently or have many partners.

Reich found that it was quality, not quantity, that made the difference. It was a person's capacity to enjoy a full sexual orgasm – he called it 'orgiastic potency' – that determined his, or her, ability to overcome neurotic behavior. It was sexual gratification, not sexual activity, that was the crucial factor.

Here, Reich's departure from Freud is significant, because, as I mentioned earlier, he saw everything in terms of energy as well as psychology.

According to Reich, neurotic behavior arises out of an individual's inability to fully discharge the energy that accumulates in the body. In other words, neurosis is nothing more, nor less, than pent-up energy seeking an avenue of release.

The natural and most healthy way of releasing energy, Reich asserted, is through sexual orgasm. It is through this essential function that the body can fully discharge its pent-up energy and begin the process of accumulation again, thereby creating a healthy pulsating rhythm of charge and discharge.

In fact, Reich divided the pulsation of orgasm into four stages: tension, charge, discharge, relaxation.

Kelley changed the order a little bit, reversing the first two stages: charge, tension, discharge, relaxation. My own experience leads me to agree with Kelley, but either way the basic formula is the same.

Seen from the perspective of this formula, it is easy to understand why a sexually dysfunctional person becomes neurotic: he never gets to the fourth stage; he never has the opportunity to relax. He is incapable of fully discharging his energy and so the unreleased energy remains in the body, manifesting as tension, restlessness, unease.

It is this unexpressed energy that, quite literally, drives a person nuts.

Underlying Reich's revolutionary approach was his discovery that, in everyday life, the body accumulates more energy than it normally uses. He speculated that this habit of building up an energy reserve was developed during human evolution as a survival mechanism – a reserve tank of gas should always be available in case of a sudden emergency requiring intense physical activity, such as flight from danger, or fighting an enemy.

In terms of energy, Reich perceives the human organism as a sphere with a core and a periphery. There is, he asserts, a certain pressure inside the sphere, because energy is gathering at the core and wants to expand, while the job of the periphery is to hold the energy in.

At a certain level of charge, the energetic pressure gets too much and begins to moves outwards from the core of its own accord, pushing towards an external sexual object as a way to relieve the pressure and regulate the level of energy inside the sphere.

It doesn't sound very romantic, but, in physical terms, it is the sensation of pressure inside the body that pushes us to press up against another body that is similarly charged – to come right up against another body and rub against it – so that the two charges can bring themselves to a climax and find release.

How does the orgasm formula work in practice?

Let's say you're walking down the street, shopping on a Saturday morning, and you pause to look at a window display in your favorite boutique. Someone else is also looking and, as you turn to go, this 'someone' says, "Hi."

You look around and see a guy whom you met, quite casually, a couple of weeks back at a friend's birthday party. You remember thinking, at the time, "Hmm, interesting man," and now here he is, standing in front of you and, yes, he seems to be inviting you across the street for a cup of coffee.

You hear yourself say, "Sure, why not?" And here you are, sitting with a decaf latte in front of you, making conversation.

Maybe you haven't noticed, but your breathing pulsation has already subtly changed its rhythm. It's become a little deeper, a little faster. You are taking in more energy, start to feel more awake, more alert, more interested in life.... Maybe you're sitting in a different way, a little more upright, not slumped over the table.

In other words, you are moving into the first stage of the orgasm formula, as understood by Kelley and myself, with the pressure of an energy charge beginning to build inside your body.

There are many different steps that lead towards love-making. Through flirting, dinner dates, dancing, intimate conversations, making out…through all the usual rituals that surround a growing attraction between two sexual beings. We can also call it 'foreplay.' But the bottom line is that a steady build-up of excitement and energy continues in both partners.

Tension also begins to enter the equation. There is a certain sense of 'holding back' that we may experience on a psychological level as, for example, not wanting to rush into the sex act too quickly, letting things take their time, not wanting to appear too 'eager,' checking out the love partner….

At the same time, we don't want the excitement to diminish. We want to hold onto the energy and so tension enters the equation, creating a balance between these two opposing forces – desire for gratification and wanting to contain the excitement.

If the attraction is allowed to move towards its natural destination, close physical contact starts to occur and, even before sexual intercourse – just body to body, without penetration – there is a quantum leap in excitement as two partners recognize, 'this is it, now we're going the whole way.'

Penetration of the penis into the vagina focuses the energy more concentratedly in the area of our sexual organs and takes the charging to a higher level. As love-making proceeds, a strong dynamic tension is created between the need of the rising tide of energy to be released and a simultaneous desire to contain, prolong and even increase the excitement.

Although scientific instruments were quite primitive in the 1920's, Reich did what he could to measure the charge of energy at different stages, including taking electrical readings from the surface of the skin. In his own way, he preceded both Alfred Kinsey and Masters and Johnson, who are widely credited as the first pioneers in scientifically researching human sexual behavior.

In his book, "Function of the Orgasm," Reich goes into great detail, describing the friction of the bodies, the increasing energy charge, the transmission of bio-electrical currents through plasma, mucus membranes and musculature.

Pursuing the image of a sphere, he uses the example of a bladder filled to bursting point with air as a way of illustrating the extreme tension of containment that occurs immediately prior to orgasm.

I must say, when I first read this section of his description, I found it rather off-putting. A bladder, ready to burst? Personally, I'd have preferred him to find a different way to illustrate the functioning of my treasured orgasms.

But his point is clear: there comes a moment when the human organism is simply incapable of containing the sexual charge any longer. Either it must burst, or it must discharge the accumulated energy.

At this critical moment, all control is lost. The point of no return is reached. Love-making changes from a voluntary process into an involuntary one. The energy floods out in orgasmic release and the whole organism goes into convulsions, with all kinds of bio-electrical currents flashing through plasma and tension draining out of the muscles.

Reich placed great emphasis on the need for an involuntary stage in orgasm if the energy is to be fully discharged. Any kind of 'doing,' technique, or method of control needs to be abandoned. The organism itself must take over and go into involuntary convulsions if a fully satisfying orgasm is going to occur.

These involuntary convulsions are, as I have already indicated, an electrical phenomenon. Those of you who have conducted experiments in school biology class will know that if an electrode containing a small electrical current is touched to the leg of a dead frog, the muscles will jump, or convulse, causing the leg to kick.

In the human body, it is the same. Our muscles respond to bio-electric currents that pass through them. In orgasm, the sex center acts like a lightning rod, like an internal electrode, and as energy pours out through the genitals the sudden charge of bio-electricity causes the body's musculature to go into rhythmic convulsions.

After the orgasm is over, the two partners involved in the love act enter a state of deep relaxation. All energy has been discharged and there is no tension remaining in the body. This explains why, after good love-making, many people tend to drift off into sleep.

In reality, many people are not capable of enjoying and allowing a full sexual orgasm, and the reasons for this are explained in the following chapter. What I wish to emphasize here is the natural process of charge and discharge, because it is this process that provides the key to Pulsation – the work I do in my groups and individual sessions.

Emotional energy follows the same pattern as sexual energy. Or, to be more accurate, I should say that energy follows the same pattern, whether it is expressed sexually or emotionally. A charge can be built in the energy body and used to trigger emotional release, which in turn can be followed by a deep sense of relaxation and well-being.

To illustrate how this works in practice, I can do no better than describe my first experience of a Reichian session, which occurred in Santa Monica, close to Los Angeles, in April 1971.

I'd become interested in Reich's ideas and had already attended a lecture in San Francisco by Charles Kelley, a scientist and psychologist who – as I mentioned in chapter one – had personally studied with Reich in the 1950's.

Together with his wife, Erica, Kelley was applying and developing Reich's principles in the area of emotional health. He called his approach 'Radix Neo-Reichian Education,' and was offering public workshops at his Radix Institute in Southern California.

Fresh out of university, with a degree in philosophy and political science, I was in the mood for adventure, and was sufficiently intrigued by Kelley's lecture to drive down the coast from San Francisco to participate in a weekend group.

About twelve people turned up and one of the first things I noticed was that, at 22, I was the youngest participant. Most were in their thirties, forties and fifties, and many were already engaged in the health and healing professions – nurses, doctors, therapists, of one kind or another.

On the first morning, the Kelleys led us through a series of intense physical exercises: breathing, jumping, shouting, huffing and puffing through seemingly impossible stress positions – only later did I learn that this particular form of self-torture is called bio-energetics.

In the afternoon, the mood changed, and Erica Kelly began to invite people to participate in one-on-one sessions with her, while the rest of us watched. After two or three others had gone before, I suddenly had the feeling it was my turn.

"Laura, would you like to be next?" asked Erica, as if reading my thoughts.

"Oh my God," I breathed silently to myself, stomach churning with nervousness and excitement.

"Yes, okay," I said, peeling down to the two-piece bathing suit which I felt much too fat to be wearing.

I lay down, my back resting on a padded mat, looked up into Erica's dark brown eyes, and then at my fellow group members who were sitting in a circle, gazing down at me expectantly and with some sympathy.

"Good. Now bend your knees, so your feet are flat and grounded on the mat, and close your eyes," Erica said gently, sitting by my side.

"Open your mouth and begin to breathe all the way down into your belly," she continued, placing her hand there, where my breathing was meant to go.

I inhaled deeply into the belly, then exhaled all the air from the chest. In...out...deeper in...deeper out...continuously, for about ten minutes.

Although I didn't know it at the time, I was being guided into building up a charge of energy, raising the potential for a discharge.

Energy. What really underlies that word? I was about to find out.

"Yes, Laura, good," encouraged Erica, pressing her hand firmly into my chest as I exhaled.

"Now, as you breathe out, make the sound *'Ohhhhh...'* and in...and then *'Ohhhhh...'* and in...and *'Ohhhhh.'*"

I began to feel a strange tingling sensation in my hands and around my mouth, which started to pucker into a tight 'O'

34

shape, quite involuntarily, as my throat tightened against a feeling which seemed to be forcing its way up from the area around my heart.

Somehow Erica seemed to know what was happening. She started vigorously massaging my throat, jaw, and shoulders, while at the same time suggesting that I allow my body to move in whatever way it wanted.

In response, my body started to make undulating movements, seemingly taking on a life of its own.

Suddenly, a voice at the very back of my mind urgently whispered, *'My dear, you are about to lose it – and in front of all these people!'*

I ignored the voice and kept on breathing.

Each breath took me deeper and deeper into a rhythm of pulsating movements and sounds that seemed to reach deeper still, giving me the feeling that I was being carried by a tide, or a river...a river that was reaching and striving towards a crescendo of feeling...and suddenly I burst loudly into tears, sobbing as if my heart could break. My bewildered mind tried to find a reason why I was crying, but there was none.

My body convulsed as the muscles started to release what felt like a lifetime of pain, grief, and longing. Slowly, I began to identify the feeling of never having received as much love as I needed or wanted, especially from men – first, from my father, then from the various boyfriends in my life.

Suddenly, memories flooded my mind: all the times in my life when I wanted *more*, and was left in a state of unfulfilled desire and longing. Ever since I can remember I was afraid to ask for anything from a man: more warmth, more intimacy and closeness. And yes, more sex.

Again, Erica's intuition blew my mind as she guided me: "Let your hands and arms reach upwards and say *'I want...I want...'*"

I grabbed onto these words like a drowning person, screaming them out in a voice I hardly recognized.

Erica's hands touched my body in just the right way to support what was happening and her gentle voice encouraged me, saying, "Yes, just let it all go...yes."

Gradually the deluge of emotion subsided. It was replaced by a feeling of expansion so vast that my arms felt like they could embrace the sky, a feeling that I *have* received everything I need. My breathing returned to normal, though it felt delightfully freer and looser.

Silently, I rested in this space, my body vibrating with a new aliveness that seemed to emanate from my belly.

After a few minutes, Erica invited me to open my eyes and look at the others around the circle.

I was welcomed back with lopsided smiles and glistening eyes which let me know these people had been with me all the way. As their hands softly touched my body, sweet laughter rippled through me and the other members of the group, helping me to relax even more.

Looking back, I think what impressed me most about that first session was the depth of relaxation I felt after the emotional release. This was something totally new. I'd never felt anything like it before.

It was direct personal experience of Reich's basic insight: in the four-beat cycle of the orgasm formula, you cannot really experience relaxation unless you are able to fully discharge the excess energy in your body – here, 'body' is used as a collective term, referring to two deeply inter-related bodies, the physical and the energetic.

A full discharge requires, in turn, a deliberate effort to build up the charge, by breathing in the manner I described, which can trigger an emotional outburst and catharsis.

I was so impressed by the power and transformative effect of the Kelleys' work that I moved to Santa Monica and trained with them over a period of two years in order to become a Reichian practitioner. To be correct, I should use the term 'Neo-Reichian' because this was how Kelley distinguished himself from the more orthodox and traditional followers of Reich.

Going through my own Neo-Reichian therapy and later working with it as a therapist, I tasted and understood how this approach works directly with sexual energy.

It moves something inside that can be called pleasurable, that can be called orgasmic. It is a sensation of filling up with energy, moving the energy and discharging it, and the relaxation that comes when one stops holding back the energy is certainly very pleasurable and you can feel the quality of sexuality in it.

Not that one gets genitally turned on in emotional release work. It's more a feeling of being orgasmically alive, feeling a flow of pleasurable sensations throughout the body.

But there was also a direct pay off in the area of my sexuality. During my first six months of working intensively with the Kelleys, I noticed that the depth of sexual experience with my lover was enhanced: more sexual energy was available, I was less distracted by thinking *about* sex – what to do next, etc. – and my orgasms were stronger and more satisfying.

Becoming a Neo-Reichian practitioner opened many doors for me in terms of deepening my understanding of this kind of work, and it is worth taking a moment to describe how this happened.

About a year after my training was complete, I was fortunate enough to become a resident therapist at the Esalen Institute in Big Sur, California, which in the early Seventies was a powerhouse of innovative therapy, a crossroads and meeting point for almost everyone involved in developing new methods of personal growth and self-exploration.

Fritz Perls had lived there in his last years, developing Gestalt Therapy, and therapists such as Dick Price, Will Schutz, Joan Halifax, Stan Grof, Bernard Gunther, Gabrielle Roth, Ida Rolf, and many more were either in residence or passing through at that time.

Esalen also had a spiritual dimension.

Alan Watts, the man who did much to introduce Eastern philosophies to Western thinking – especially Zen – was a frequent visitor. Aldous Huxley, who wrote about the spiritual aspect of hallucinogenic drugs in his book, 'The Doors of

Perception,' had visited Esalen several times and the institute's main group room was named in his honor.

When I arrived at Esalen, India was in fashion among a whole generation of young Americans, and travelers returning to the institute from the East were offering lectures on the chakra system, courses in yoga and many types of meditation.

Altogether, it was a heady cocktail of Western psychotherapy and Eastern spirituality, and, working and living on campus, I drank it with gusto.

At about this time, I heard of an unusual 'chaotic meditation' technique developed by an Indian mystic called Bhagwan Shree Rajneesh and it was not long before I had the opportunity to try it out.

The Kelleys had organized a European tour for me, conducting workshops in several countries, and in London I met a group of Rajneesh disciples and joined them in an hour-long experience of their chaotic technique, known as 'Dynamic Meditation.'

Until then, I had envisioned meditation as a silent, calm and relatively inactive process. One simply sat cross-legged with eyes closed, in a Buddha-like posture, and tried to quiet the mind with thoughts of compassion and peace, or else chanted secret mantras or channeled energy up the spine.

Dynamic Meditation was an utterly different experience and certainly lived up to its name. Lasting sixty minutes, it had five stages, beginning with ten minutes of strong breathing, through the nose, the mouth closed, emphasizing the exhalation.

In this opening stage, the whole body gets involved, with arms flailing by the sides, a bit like handles of an old-fashioned bellows, helping to pump air in and out of the lungs.

Breathing through the nose, pushing the air strongly out on the exhale – the reverse of our normal breathing pattern – had a curious effect on me. It was greatly energizing, but at the same time tapped into a growing feeling of frustration, impatience and anger.

Chaotic drumming music urged us on and by the time the second stage arrived, heralded by a loud gong, I was more than ready for the ten minutes of catharsis and emotional release which was now meant to happen. I was ready to pop, and screamed my head off, along with everybody else.

The third stage, again ten minutes, was extremely vigorous. We jumped up and down, with arms raised above our heads, landing on the flat of the feet, shouting the mantra "Hoo! Hoo! Hoo!"

This, we were told beforehand, acted as a combined 'hammer' on the sex center: the repetitive jumping sent impulses shooting up the legs into the genital area, while the "Hoo!" did the same with sound from within. Apparently, the intention was to awaken dormant sources of sexual energy and distribute it through the body.

After three stages and thirty minutes of intense and exhausting activity, accompanied by loud music, a voice on the audio tape suddenly declared "Stop!" and we froze in whatever position we found ourselves, not moving a muscle.

Here, we were instructed to simply 'watch,' or notice, with eyes closed, everything that was happening: the pounding of the blood in our ears, the panting of our breath – gradually slowing as we recovered from the effort – the sweat trickling down our bodies, the thoughts racing in our minds.

This silent stage lasted for fifteen minutes.

The final stage, also fifteen minutes, was for dance and celebration.

As you may have already been able to guess, what struck me about this Dynamic Meditation technique was that it contained the same essential ingredients as Reich's orgasm formula, beginning with a vigorous build up of an energy charge in the body, followed by discharge and relaxation.

I wasn't clear about the meditation aspect – I was still very 'uncooked' in terms of comprehending the whole Eastern dimension of inner experience – but I liked the enlivening effect Dynamic had on me, and also the sense of relaxation and well-being that followed.

Thus began my attraction to the teaching methods of Rajneesh, who later became known as Osho. And, although I did not know it, this was also the beginning of a gradual merging of my Reichian work with the path of Tantra.

By now, having accompanied me through descriptions of a powerful Neo-Reichian session with Erica Kelley and a strenuous hour of Dynamic, you may be wondering:

Why the need for so much effort? Why all the huffing and puffing, the breathing, the stress, the emotional floods of tears and anger? Do we really need to go through all this in order to feel happy, alive, sensual, orgasmic and relaxed?

The short answer, I'm afraid, is 'yes.'

The reasons will be made clear in the next chapter.

Chapter Four

Armoring: The Seven Segments

When I was young I was a very expressive child and, like most other little girls who grow up in so-called 'normal' families, I loved my daddy. In those early, formative years, daddy was the main man in my life.

I would sometimes really want him to hold me, or I'd reach out to him, or touch him…a child's simple longing for the feelings of warmth, closeness and reassurance that a father can give. But most of the time – almost all of the time, in fact – I was kept at a certain distance by him, which I felt as a kind of rejection.

I don't know why he did that. I know he cared about me and tried to be a good father, but maybe he was concerned that my mother or sisters would be jealous. Maybe he was afraid of his own emotions, self-conscious about showing affection, wondering what other people might think. Maybe he was afraid that he might start feeling sexual while horsing around with me.

It's hard to know what went on in his mind, but later on, after that first session with Erica Kelley, as I went deeper into my own therapy and explored the hidden parts of my psychology, I started to remember many moments of hurt, disappointment and rejection concerning my father and my longing to be close to him.

I also remembered certain moments when I steeled myself against those kinds of feelings, so that I wouldn't feel the hurt, so that it wouldn't show. I found a way to deal with it, just to save myself from pain.

Physically, this manifested as a tightening in my throat, as if I was swallowing my own voice, and also trying to hold myself together by tightening sets of muscles in my body, especially around the diaphragm and solar plexus. In this way, everything became more controlled and manageable, as if I could package the expression of my feelings in a form that was acceptable to both myself and my parents.

Of course, at the time, I had no idea what I was doing. I didn't know that certain groups of muscles could be used to stifle unwanted feelings. I just did my best to protect myself and, as a result, became less expressive, less spontaneous – less alive.

That's the price we all pay for protecting ourselves. When our muscles habitually tighten and contract, our energy shrinks because it cannot flow so easily through the body and a lifelong pattern of diminished vitality is created.

In my case, for example, my defensive habit of steeling myself against wanting anything from my father carried over into my love relationships with men as an adult. It was hard for me to be spontaneously expressive, responding freely and emotionally, showing affection, or asking for it. Both my mind and body had been trained to prevent it.

Reich first discovered the relationship between emotional control and tight muscles while working in Freud's Vienna clinic, then later in his own clinics, which he opened to the public wherever he went.

He noticed that many of his patients had a certain deadness or rigidity in the way they presented themselves physically. He observed their mannerisms: the way they didn't look directly at him when they talked, the way they talked very quietly, or didn't seem to be breathing very much, or would hunch their shoulders, or fold their arms tightly across the chest.

Gradually, he understood that people with neurosis are also contracted in their bodies in different ways, so he started to experiment. While they were talking, lying on his couch, he would touch the belly and find it to be rock hard with tension,

42

and he would encourage them, "Now breathe more deeply here, into your belly."

He met resistance in his patients, naturally, because the reason why people create tension in their bodies is to stop feeling. When they did start to breathe they also started to get upset, also getting angry at Reich for making them do this.

But, rather than trying to stop the emotion, or redirect it, he would provoke it more, encouraging this expressive energy to expand, asking the client to report any physical tightness in the body, any emotion that was surfacing, and so on.

He would ask people to notice things about themselves – that you can't say those words you want to say, that your throat is tightening and your breathing has stopped, perhaps to prevent forbidden words from coming out. And when they came out, when they exploded, he would have the person hit the couch, or move the body, or shout and scream so that the energy could be released.

After the release, he would notice that the breathing would be more relaxed and natural, that tension in certain muscle groups had also relaxed, and that energy appeared to be flowing more easily through the whole body – especially through the area that had previously been constricted.

This was part of Reich's revolution: he developed a 'hands on' approach to therapy, working with the body, the breathing, the emotion and the psychological issue at the same time.

This was a far cry from the cool analytical style of his mentor, Sigmund Freud.

Just imagine: your therapist is no longer sitting behind the couch, where you cannot see him, asking questions in a detached way and taking notes of what you are saying. Instead, he is right in your face. He is poking your body, getting you to breathe deeply, making you feel things, massaging your tight muscles, getting you ready to explode with emotion.

This was a form of therapy Freud had never imagined. But for Reich it was an essential part of curing neurosis and restoring psychological health. To him, it was not possible to change the thinking process at a deep level without changing the body as well.

In this way, Reich became the first man to take psychology beyond the mind and into the body.

One of his principle discoveries was that groups of muscles function together, assisting the expression of energy. For instance, sticking out the tongue is an expression of anger that involves the muscles of the mouth and also the upper throat. Shrinking away in fear involves collapsing the chest, pulling the shoulders forwards and inwards to protect the heart area. A sudden shock makes the eyes widen as the muscles around them pull back and contract.

Reich found that there are seven segments, or groups of muscles, that surround the body in rings, rather like the rings of a worm – in fact, he speculated that this segmental arrangement of muscles in the human body is an evolutionary hangover from our ancient worm ancestors.

It will be helpful to describe the seven segments, starting at the top of the body and moving downwards in sequence.

1. Ocular Segment (Eyes)

Located at the top of the head. It includes the eyes, the muscles within and around the eye sockets, the forehead, the top of the head, the sides of the head, and muscles underneath the ridge of the scalp at the back of the head, where the skull meets the neck.

2. Oral Segment (Mouth)

Includes the whole mouth area: lips, teeth, tongue, jaw and a group of muscles linking the jaw to the back of the neck.

3. Cervical Segment (Throat)

The third segment involves all the muscles of the neck and throat. This is a very important segment in Reichian therapy because so much energy passes through it.

There are muscles in the front of the throat connected with expression of tears, sadness, pain; muscles at the sides connected with holding or expressing anger; muscles at the back of the neck related to fear.

4. Thoracic Segment (Chest)

The chest segment includes the ribcage and follows the ribs around to the back of the body where they connect with the spine. It also includes all the muscles of the shoulders, arms and the hands.

Obviously, this segment is deeply related to our breathing, and also to the feelings of the heart.

5. Diaphragm Segment

The fifth segment involves all the muscles of the diaphragm which is sitting underneath the lungs. It is an umbrella-shaped group of muscles that drop down into the abdominal cavity with the in-breath and rise up to help the lungs to empty with the out-breath.

This segment is also is deeply connected with breathing and emotional control.

6. Abdominal Segment (Belly)

The belly segment involves all the muscles of the abdomen and the lower back. It also includes our guts – the origin of many deep feelings.

7. Pelvic Segment (Sex)

The last segment involves the muscles at the floor of the pelvis and is connected to the genitals, anus, buttocks, legs and feet. This is also our connection between the body and the earth.

As I said before, these seven muscle segments surround the body like rings, creating a tube-like effect that helps to conduct energy through the organism, reminiscent of a worm in motion.

Just as a wave of movement is transmitted through the segments of a worm in order to propel it forward along the ground, similarly a wave of energy is conducted through the body via opening and closing muscle segments that have their own rhythmic, squeezing action.

One segment, or ring of muscles, acts like a single sphincter muscle, such as the one located at the opening of the anus, or like other sphincter muscles inside the digestive tract. They open and close to allow food and waste to pass through at the required time.

Energy – especially emotional energy – is pushed through the whole body by the pulsation of the seven muscle segments, so that what is felt in one area becomes a unified expression of the whole organism.

In the body of a young child, where no chronic defense patterns have yet been formed, unified expression happens naturally and easily.

Let's say a child gets angry. The feeling may originate in his guts, and is then passed by the pulsation of the muscle segments through the chest to the throat, where it finds vocal expression and erupts from his mouth as a scream or cry of rage. He may also be hitting out with his hands, kicking with his legs, having a full-on temper tantrum that involves the whole body.

All the segments of muscles in the child's body are cooperating with the tantrum, helping the energy to move, giving it expression, allowing release.

However, if a block occurs – say the child hears "shut up" from a threatening parent – then immediately the throat, which has been making sounds, closes. The group of muscles in this segment tightens and goes into a kind of paralysis, prohibiting vocal expression.

Most probably, too, breathing is cut, or drastically reduced, to stop the heaving chest from pushing any more energy up towards the throat, and tension is created in the diaphragm and other muscles which regulate the child's breathing.

For a Reichian practitioner, the important thing to understand is that the energy now being held back doesn't just vanish into thin air. It may partially discharge as a different type of emotion, for example tears, which may be more acceptable to the parents. But the main energy charge will stay in the muscles themselves, locked in as tension, and with repetition this tension will harden and become chronic – part of the musculature.

This is why, when I touch a client's stomach, or diaphragm, or chest, I can feel – as Reich did before me – that some muscles seem to be made almost of iron. They have become steel hard as a way of protecting the client against his or her environment.

Reich called this hardening of the muscles 'armoring.' Essentially it is stored tension, blocked energy, suppressed emotion.

Not all tension in the body is armoring. Some is related purely to mechanical factors like bad posture at work: sitting at a desk all day long in front of a computer, bending forwards and hunching the shoulders. This is going to create tension in the neck, shoulders, back and upper torso.

But we also carry many, many tensions that are emotionally related and can be traced back to childhood trauma. This is the 'armoring' we carry.

I like the term, because it is graphically illustrative of the shape most people are in when they come to me, rather like old fashioned knights from medieval tales who have put on a suit of armor for battle and now cannot get it off.

Unfortunately, however, the situation is more complicated. With a good tool kit of spanners, saws and wrenches, a suit of armor can be stripped off and the human being inside released from his prison.

The armor we carry is inside us, within the muscles themselves, and has become part of our whole energy system and its habitual patterns.

Moreover, the muscles are not dead like armor plating. They are still alive. The segments still do their job of passing energy, but the flow is drastically reduced. The impulses to express emotion are still present, but the tension that holds them back is usually stronger.

This brings me to an important point: the seven segments don't just block energy flow. In certain circumstances, they actively push in the opposite direction. This opposing movement is called a 'counter-pulsation.'

To see how this works, let's go back for a moment to the image of a ringed segmental tube. Imagine that the energy in the tube in increasing and seeking expressive release. It could be tears, it could be anger – it could also be an expression of love – but whatever the case it is growing and moving.

In a naturally functioning organism, all seven segments support this flow of energy and help to give it expression and release.

However, in an armored body, as the energy surges upward and outward it will meet a wall of tension. Perhaps, as in my own case, the desire to reach out for love was checked in childhood and now the diaphragm and chest muscles are trained to hold it back.

At least one of the rings of muscles around our inner tube, which should be squeezing rhythmically to assist expression, will now go against it, pushing in the opposite direction, trying to squeeze the energy back down.

This is counter-pulsation. It is a pulsation of a part that is moving against the pulsation of the whole organism. Not surprisingly, it disturbs the harmonious flow of energy through the body, creating a fragmentation effect rather than helping to unify expression.

At a biological and energetic level, counter-pulsation reflects a human personality that is divided against itself – a kind of schizophrenic split between a natural impulse to express and a learned response to block it.

As a result, the rings in the upper part of the body may be expressing one type of feeling, while the lower segments are saying something entirely different. On a personality or thinking level, we experience a mixed message:

"I want this, but on the other hand I'm afraid of the consequences."

"This really feels good to me, but I feel I'm not supposed to be doing it."

These double messages create double-binds in our energy flow and we can easily feel stuck, caught between opposing impulses, unable to move or express anything with totality.

At first glance, it looks as though counter-pulsation is 'a bad thing,' because it works against the natural flow of energy.

For the therapist, however, it is important to remember that counter-pulsation is also an expression of our vitality. It has a positive intention. Originally, it arose out of our instinctual intelligence, as children, to protect ourselves in the best possible way in critical situations – for example, to stop crying when threatened with physical punishment.

It is life energy that has turned back against itself.

This 'decision' to hold back energy and emotion arises out of our capacity to judge what kind of behavior is acceptable and what is not. It is learned through experience in childhood and youth, becomes habitual and, with time, so automatic that we don't even notice we are doing it.

It explains why human beings have armoring and animals do not. Animals don't discriminate in this way. They don't hold back their energy or feelings. Energetically, they live simple, straightforward lives, as in, for example, the most basic instinct of 'fight or flight.'

It is only human beings who, caught in the complex web of deciding what kinds of expression are socially acceptable, gradually build up an armored defense system.

There are two related but distinctive processes happening in an armored body.

First, on a day to day level, the armoring diminishes the energy flow and this is an almost universal phenomenon in modern society – everyone is in more or less the same condition.

You may be running on, say, twenty percent of your capacity, but, as you go to work or perform the everyday functions of life, you are not aware of this chronic crippling effect. This is 'normal.' This is how it's always been, at least in adult life.

Second, the armoring may, at any time, need to kick into another gear and create a counter-pulsation. For example, today, at work, your supervisor starts to behave like a real asshole and suddenly you feel a burning anger in your solar plexus and an impulse to scream, "Fuck off!"

However, your intelligent and discriminating mind immediately informs you of the consequences of following such an impulse: most probably you will be fired and right now that's not a good option. Your credit cards are maxed out, the rent is due, your girlfriend's birthday is only two days away and you need every cent you can earn.

As the rising energy of anger pushes its way through your diaphragm and into your chest, seeking expression, your financial situation is saved by the cervical segment. Muscles in your throat tighten into a clamp-like grip on your vocal chords, strangling the curse you are about to utter.

The energy is pushed back down the tube. Your job is saved. But you pay a severe price: your life force is once again being suffocated.

Perhaps I should mention here that, according to Charles Kelley, armoring is not always a negative phenomenon. He asserts that armoring can be used creatively in order to attain long-term goals by inhibiting short-term gratification.

When I'm working with a client, I often see counter-pulsation in action: how an expressive wave of energy starts to move from the lower segments, runs up against a wall of armoring, is prevented from continuing upwards and turns back on itself.

There are special exercises I do, when training people, that can help them observe how counter-pulsation happens.

I have people work in pairs. One partner plays the client, lying on his or her back, on a mat, knees raised and feet flat on the floor, in the basic breathing position. The other partner plays the observing therapist, sitting by the side of the mat.

I invite the person who is lying down to begin a soft, deep, breathing pulsation, filling the lungs, expanding the chest, inhaling all the way down into the belly and then exhaling fully.

After a while, I ask them to add a movement of the body, in the same rhythm as the breathing.

As they breathe in, the back arches and the pelvis pulls back, pressing the tailbone into the mat. The backswing of the pelvis makes space for energy, riding on the in-breath, to come down into the belly.

When they breathe out, the pelvis rocks forward and up, in a kind of sexual thrust, so the tail bone comes off the mat. As the pelvis pushes forward, it also pushes the wave of energy and breath back up the body, out through the mouth.

This basic combination of breathing and movement, which I call Soft Pulsation, helps to create a wave of energy that begins to flow up and down the body.

In a body that can allow this pulsatory flow, the wave continues and becomes even stronger as the breathing and movement intensifies.

But in an armored body, what we notice is that, as a charge of energy builds up, certain sets of muscles start to become tense, instinctively beginning to do their job of holding back too big a charge.

For example, as the pelvis swings forward and the energy travels up the body, we may notice the diaphragm is starting to tighten in order to prevent the energy from coming out through the mouth.

As the energy charge intensifies, the muscles in the diaphragm respond by becoming more and more tense, and soon you can see the counter-pulsation at work, moving against the natural direction and flow. The diaphragm is trying to push the wave back down into the belly.

It's rather like watching ripples on the surface of a calm lake. You throw one pebble and ripples begin to spread out across the lake. You throw another, some distance away, and the new

51

ripples also spread out. At a certain point the two sets of ripples meet, hit each other, and send a counter-wave back in the opposite direction.

Part of the ripple continues in the original direction and it's the same in the human organism. For example, the diaphragm may allow some of the energy through and, in order to ensure that blocking happens and expression is cut, the throat will also tighten. Often, the diaphragm and throat work together in their holding patterns, like a team.

Sometimes, to the therapist, it appears as if you are holding a snake by the middle – the two ends, the head and the tail, are wiggling, but in the place where you are holding it, the snake is immobile. Similarly, in the human organism, you can see energy moving below the armored block and you can also see it moving above, but at the block itself everything is frozen, as if gripped by an unseen hand.

I have referred several times to armoring in the diaphragm and throat, because these are critical segments in controlling expression, but they are not the only places where a counter-pulsation occurs. It can happen anywhere, in any of the segments.

Sometimes, in this exercise, the pelvis itself starts to automatically reverse, moving against the natural pulsation. Without knowing it, the client – the partner who is breathing – has reversed the rocking action: now the pelvis pushes forward on the in-breath and swings back on the out-breath. This is a clear counter-pulsation in the pelvic segment that is unconsciously saying 'no' to the energy and its expression.

This exercise helps trainees identify counter-pulsations, so they can see them in action and understand the principle before launching into the de-armoring process. And it is a good way to discover where the main armoring is located, how the body is holding and blocking energy.

However, as in most disciplines, there is a significant difference between theory and practice, and I don't want to give the impression that working with the breathing pulsation, orgasm formula and seven armored segments is an exact science.

Reichian therapy is not as obvious and straightforward as such concepts make it sound. It's more like an art. When I'm working with a client, I'm using the basic principles I've absorbed in my training and work experience, but I'm also working spontaneously and intuitively.

A client may have several different pulsations and counter-pulsations moving in the body – I may see several splits in the energy at once – and then it's a question of figuring out where to begin, how to solve the puzzle, dissolve the tension, unify the energy, heal the organism.

It's an individual affair, not a mathematical equation. There are similarities that cut across all national, cultural, ethnic and religious backgrounds, but each person is unique. Each human organism has a different configuration of armoring, each client has a different psychology, a different life story.

By now, I hope it is clear why I asserted, at the end of the previous chapter, that a certain amount of intense effort is needed to restore a human organism to its natural state of wholeness, health and happiness.

We need to undo the damage. We need to dissolve the armoring, so that our energy can flow freely, emotions can be felt, sexuality can be accepted and enjoyed. And, by the way, the type of armoring I have described so far – such as my reaction to my father's emotional and physical distance – is nothing compared to what many people experience as they grow up.

Physical abuse, condemnation of sexuality, denial of emotion, sexual abuse, cruelty, bullying, manipulation, teasing, lack of love, neglect, isolation, abandonment.... It all impacts the muscle segments and gets stored as tension, blocked energy, hardening the armor that surrounds the body.

Dissolving this armor is a challenging road to personal liberation and, as far as I know, there are no short cuts.

Chapter Five

The Feeling Pairs

If you break down the word 'emotion' into its component parts – 'e' and 'motion' – you can see that it was originally formed from Latin roots to indicate a movement outwards. This definition suits the Reichian understanding of human emotions. Fundamentally, emotions are seen as nothing but a movement of plasma, a wave of energy that passes through the liquid contents of the body, seeking expression and release.

Such a detached view may not mean much to us, when we are weeping over a lost lover, or getting angry about some offensive remark, but it certainly helps the Reichian therapist to understand the mechanics of restoring a healthy pulsation in the body of a client and opening the doors to happiness, greater vitality and a sense of well-being.

Reich himself took emotion back to its most primitive and basic form, using the example of a single cell organism, the amoeba. Observing through a microscope, he saw that the plasma inside the cell of an amoeba pushes out towards pleasure and retracts in anxiety from pain.

It is a two-way movement, or, as he liked to call it, a two-way 'emotion of the protoplasm.'

The impulse towards pleasure creates a movement from the core of the cell towards the periphery, while the impulse to avoid pain creates a movement in the opposite direction, a shrinking back from the periphery towards the core.

This, he declared, is the basic, two-stroke pulsation of all living organisms and the origin of human expression: we all want to feel pleasure; we all want to avoid pain.

Reich also pointed out that expressive movement is an inherent characteristic of living organisms, distinguishing them from the rest of nature. To be alive is to move, to move is to express.

It all looks very obvious, but the implication is significant: like it or not, we are, all of us, emotional beings. Feelings are part of the package called 'life' and the emotional expression of those feelings is a natural and essential movement of our energy.

If we stifle them, suppress them, we are stifling the life force itself.

From this perspective, it is not difficult to see the basic conflict that has arisen between human nature and our so-called civilized attitudes. In 'advanced' societies, the less emotion one shows, the more civilized one is deemed to be.

It reminds me of the famous 'stiff upper lip' attitude, prevalent in the days of the British Empire, in which *not* to show emotion in times of extreme stress was considered to be the height of good manners and civilized behavior.

I can't remember the exact quote, but I recall reading a diary entry by a British lady, made during the Indian Mutiny in 1857, while enduring a long siege in Lucknow, that "Major So-and-so was decapitated by a cannon ball this morning whilst shaving." Her diary was like that: a meticulous record of the horrors of a siege with emotions rigidly suppressed.

We Americans are not quite so good at concealing emotion, but the general attitude remains the same. For example, I remember joking with my sisters that we all belong to the 'Fine Family' – 'Fine' was our real name, not Dillon – because every time we asked each other, "How are you?" the answer was always, "Fine!"

That's the American way: look good, keep smiling and be sure to have a nice day. And if any unwanted, negative emotions start creeping in behind the 'I'm okay' façade, there's always the latest derivative of prozac or valium available to neutralize them. Of course, those clever little pills will destroy your capacity for happiness as well as misery, but that's a price most people are prepared to pay in order to keep things nice and normal.

It's not just Caucasians who have this attitude. Sophisticated cultures at any point in history, including Japan, China, Egypt and India, have required strict formality in social interaction that usually prohibits the expression of feelings.

Reich's message to the world is that this civilizing process has gone way too far in the direction of emotional control. The cost is too high, in terms of creating neurotic human beings who cannot really enjoy life.

This is particularly true today. Human ingenuity has, through the development of science, succeeded in creating a comfortable world filled with all kinds of technological marvels that make work easy and offer all kinds of leisure activities, but the parallel crushing of the life force has made us almost incapable of enjoying our own achievements.

We have to reclaim our emotions in order to restore our love of life.

With this aim in mind, Charles Kelley took Reich's basic 'pleasure-anxiety' pulsation and developed a more sophisticated model for working with his clients.

Instead of just one pair of feelings, he discovered that it is more accurate, and more helpful, to view emotions in terms of three 'feeling pairs.'

The three 'feeling pairs' are:

Anger-Love
Fear-Trust
Pain-Pleasure

The three negative emotions – anger, fear and pain – are each related to a different aspect of pulsation. Anger is associated with the outward movement from core to periphery. Fear is related to the inward movement, from periphery to core. Pain is related to the convulsive quality of energy discharge, the rapid contraction and expansion of muscles that we experience in events like laughing, sobbing and orgasm.

Each negative emotion, when blocked, has a characteristic way of holding itself in the body in the form of muscular tensions. This enables an experienced therapist to 'read' the body of a client and detect the predominant blocked emotion.

To a certain degree we can classify people as anger types, fear types, or pain types, and this is helpful in deciding how to begin the process of releasing blocked emotions and restoring a healthy pulsation.

However, this doesn't mean that anger types are the only people who get angry. We all have the full spectrum of emotions inside us. It is just an indication of the kind of habits that have been formed over the years, and which type of emotion is predominantly blocked.

The three positive emotions are also related to pulsation. Love flows out towards other people from core to periphery. Trust is a form of receptivity, allowing the outside world to penetrate inwards. Pleasure is a state of well-being involving the whole organism.

As we shall see, the fact that negative and positive emotions both relate to pulsation has profound implications, because misunderstandings about how to treat negative emotions directly impact our capacity to experience positive ones as well.

Anger – Love

Anger is an out-flowing energy. You can see this very easily in the way fights develop, especially among men. For example, two guys in a bar are talking about football. One says that the San Francisco 49ers are the best team in the world and the other snorts in disgust and replies, "These days, the Niners ain't worth a damn."

Immediately the first man feels personally insulted, gets angry and lets fly with a punch to the other man's jaw. A classic 'bar room brawl' is under way.

Anger is a hard, explosive and aggressive expression of energy – a sudden rush from core to periphery – so in a fight the fist is really nothing but an extension of an energetic impulse, traveling outwards.

The same is true of guns. When, in an old-fashioned western movie, two cowboys get into a fight and 'grab iron,' the blazing guns are an extension of the same energy, and so are the bullets. This, by the way, is why so many people die in the United States from gunshot wounds. It is the availability and proximity of weapons as a means of extending the energetic impulse of anger.

As civilized beings, however, we are instructed from childhood not to express anger and, generally speaking, we do our best to contain it. This effort, motivated by the best intentions, creates tension and hardening in the muscles.

The armoring of anger is located at the periphery of the body, because the energy is on its way out when it gets stopped. In a typical anger type, you will see strong hands and arms with rigid muscles, a lot of tension around the mouth and jaw, a barrel chest that sticks out as if challenging the world to attack it.

There is a sense of thinly contained emotion about such people, as if you need only to bump into them, or tread on their toes, or say the wrong thing, and they will immediately explode.

As I just mentioned, social education teaches us to block anger – except in specific situations such as war – but the difficulty with this attitude is that it also prevents love.

Love is a soft, tender, compassionate expression of the outward movement of our energy. Although they are very different, love and anger ride the same highway, moving in the same direction, from core to periphery.

If one aspect of outward expression is blocked, it tends also to block the other aspect as well. And love is a much softer, more delicate feeling. It will not be able to pass through the hard layer of chronic tension created by the habit of blocking anger.

Even if, at your core, you long to express your love, to reach out towards others in an expansive movement, you cannot. The highway is jammed, the traffic is blocked, nothing can move.

Here is the classic dilemma created by social morality. We are told not to be angry, but rather to be loving and compassionate – we are instructed to 'love thy neighbor' and 'turn the other cheek' – without any understanding of the energy dynamics involved.

It is just not possible to suppress anger and be loving. Yes, you can reduce love to an idea, to an intellectual concept, and pretend that you love others, that you love humanity, that you care for the poor and the downtrodden.

But real, warm, heartfelt love is a living energy that requires movement and expression, and if the avenue of expression is blocked by an armored body, it will never be able to reach the other person.

Anger needs to be released and expressed in order for love to flow.

Because of wrong education, people don't know what to do with anger, but the solution is very simple: anger needs to be thrown out and that's it – that's the only thing that will help. It is an outward moving wave of energy that needs to be expressed and discharged.

Of course, this doesn't mean that we should all start screaming at each other, getting into fights and carrying guns. There are safe, intelligent ways to release anger that do not harm others: we can go into a room, by ourselves, pick up a pillow and smash it against the floor, or beat it with our fists; we can do a meditation technique like Dynamic that invites emotional expression; we can scream when alone in a car, with the windows rolled up – although this requires a degree of care and alertness in order to prevent accidents (it's better to park first).

Once anger has been discharged and the internal highway is clear, there is a much greater possibility for love to also flow and find expression.

This explains why, in some long-term relationships, men and women develop a habit of quarreling before making love – 'fighting and fucking' as it is sometimes called. Without knowing it, they are trying to clear away the blocked energy so they can feel the love waiting behind it.

60

In the past, it has not been easy for women to express anger directly. In Victorian times, for example, tight corsets and restrictive clothing mirrored a parallel state of strict emotional confinement.

The underlying belief was that, no matter how justified a woman's anger may be, the man will always be stronger and keep her down, forcing her to choke back her rage.

More often than not, a woman's anger was released through a kind of hysterical fit – a form of helpless anger. Hysteria was one of the most common psychological problems encountered by the Freudians as they began to investigate the female psyche, at the beginning of the twentieth century. Today, it is not much of an issue, which is a tribute to the liberation of women and their right to express emotion directly.

The other traditional female method of dealing with this energy is nagging, which, though successful in reducing men to the status of henpecked husbands, is really a perverted form of anger. As with hysteria, it developed from an inability to express the emotion directly.

Fear - Trust

Fear makes people shrink. It is a contractive, inward pulling of energy, because really your basic survival instinct is saying, "Run away!" It is the urge to take yourself out of a situation that is perceived as dangerous. Adrenaline is released into the body to promote action and the animal inside you wants to run, to flee.

In some situations, flight is a practical and possible option. We have all seen video footage and photographs from 9/11/2001, showing hundreds of people fleeing through the streets of Manhattan to escape from the collapsing twin towers of the World Trade Center.

Suddenly, civilized behavior usually associated with suits, ties, briefcases and the business lifestyle was forgotten as the animal instinct took over and made people run for their lives.

With the upbringing of young children, however, it is a different story. They find themselves in scary family situations from which they are unable to flee. They are helpless, dependent on the very people – most commonly mom and dad – who are making them afraid. They cannot get away and so, instead of making them flee, fear makes children shrink.

Essentially, this shrinking is an energetic retreat to the core, an inward movement, an attempt to escape from the periphery where the danger lies. It can be triggered by a thousand and one incidents, but basically it reflects an unsafe domestic environment in which the child has to be alert to protect itself.

Unpredictability is a key element in the fear equation. It's not that dad, or mom, is angry all the time, but the tendency of one or both parents to suddenly explode creates an atmosphere of continuous anxiety, a constant wondering about 'when is it going to happen?'

It may be because father is an alcoholic who becomes physically abusive when drunk. It may be because mother is nervous and cannot handle stress beyond a certain point, whereupon she suddenly 'loses it' and starts slapping the kids around.

In my experience, based on working with many clients, some fear types are actually created in the womb, because here, especially, it's impossible to run away.

For instance, in the case of a mother who would have preferred not to be pregnant, her unspoken wish to abort the child creates a climate of fear to which the fetus responds. Similarly, if the mother is in a continuous state of stress, or feeling fear and anxiety during the pregnancy, this communicates to the fetus and brings about a fearful questioning: "Is it safe to be here? Do I have a right to be here?"

These kinds of responses are not at a thinking level – the fetus has no knowledge of language – but are experienced at a primitive, instinctive organismic level, creating the tendency to shrink energetically.

Fear types can also be created shortly after birth, within the first year-and-a-half of life, during the so-called 'oral stage,' when the infant is in its most helpless condition, dependent on the mother for 24-hour care.

If this close relationship with the mother is disturbed, if the feeding and caring routine is significantly disrupted by any kind of abandonment, rejection, anger – or maybe just irritation from changing too many diapers – the same tendency to shrink will occur.

It's not that the mother needs to have any bad intention. Maybe there is a screaming three year-old at her feet, demanding attention, while she's trying to change the new baby's nappies, and because her attention is distracted she accidentally jabs a pin in the baby's thigh.

This kind of thing, if it happens often enough, will create the impression of an unsafe environment which in turn creates fear.

Fear is an interesting phenomenon, because not only do you want to get away from the source of danger, or pain, you also want to get away from the feeling of fear itself.

Being afraid is an uncomfortable experience. It's a sensation of shrinking, the logical conclusion of which is that if you shrink too much you will disappear altogether and die. So the fear-oriented child also armors itself against this feeling.

As a result, armoring of a fear type lies deep inside, around the core of the body.

This represents two tendencies:

First, the retreat of energy from the periphery, where danger lies.

Second, the protection of the core against the shrinking movement.

In anger, as we have seen, armoring happens at the periphery, to prevent striking outwards. In fear, a kind of frozenness happens deep inside, so that that inward rush of energy from the periphery doesn't completely overwhelm the core.

In appearance, fear types tend to look thin and fragile because energy is being held at the center. They tend to have weak muscles in the arms and legs, and the chest may be hollow, with a collapsed look. Often, energy is also withdrawn from the eyes, so that they can be near-sighted or myopic.

It is understandable that this type of person has difficulty trusting people or the surrounding environment, because trust requires openness and receptivity. Trust is a decision to allow energy from outside to penetrate you.

Like fear, trust rides on the inward pulsation, moving from periphery to core, so it follows that if a person is armored against fear this blocking will also prevent the soft, receiving, inflow of trust.

One of the first steps in dealing with fear is to help a client recognize and accept it, and this means sinking down into the core, where the fear lies. It's a more delicate task than working with anger, because a fear type needs to feel safe – needs to already have a certain amount of trust – in order to allow a deeper inward movement of energy.

The discharge of fear is not as obvious as the release of anger. It usually comes through high screams, and the capacity to trust is regained slowly as the inner armoring begins to break up and tension is released.

At a psychological level, trust means you can relax with other people without having a chronic pattern of suspicion, such as, "this person appears to be friendly but that's only because he wants to get something from me…"

This doesn't mean trust has to be unconditional or blind. If there are genuine grounds for suspicion, if a situation is becoming strange or dangerous, it's healthy to be able to discriminate and take defensive measures.

But, basically, trust is an attitude that "the world is not out to get me. I can move through life in an open and relaxed way, letting things affect me, touch me, reach me."

This is one of the important outcomes of Reichian work: it helps the client regain the capacity to open and close appropriately. When there's reason to fear, defenses can be put up. When it's okay to trust, they can be let down.

When a small child is really crying or laughing its whole body is in a state of healthy and natural pulsation. But when these feelings are suppressed and blocked, the pulsation is diminished, so that both the inward and outward movements are minimized in an effort to deaden unwanted or unacceptable feelings.

In the pain type, every effort is made *not* to feel, *not* to recognize what wants to be expressed. It's a kind of holding, or suspension, of the pulsation.

This happens when a child's feelings are hurt – for example, by being called names and being pushed away by other children, or being ostracized by one's own family for some offense and being made to stand alone in a corner while all the attention and love of the parents goes to other siblings.

I remember that, in my own childhood, I was very angry with my younger sister, who was born two years after me, because suddenly she was getting all the attention that had, until her arrival, been directed exclusively at me.

I hated her and often behaved in quite a horrible way towards her, so my parents, in an effort to protect her, would ostracize me. Then I would be left with my rage and my tears, which could not be expressed, and slowly, slowly I learned to numb myself against them.

Anger and fear both have a clear direction – anger outward, fear inward – but in the blocking of pain, both strokes of the pulsation are contracted in the effort to feel less, and slowly, slowly, the whole organism becomes insensitive.

As we have seen, anger types carry a strong charge of energy at the periphery, while fear types keep it at the core. Pain types carry a strong charge all the way through the body, from core to periphery.

As a result, these people can be tireless workers, with an incredible stamina to keep going – they can swim laps at the local pool long after everyone else has given up – but all this activity does not create a sense of vitality.

On the contrary, they have an air of stagnation about them and also tend to be overweight, because the accumulation of fat in areas of tension helps to deaden the feelings.

For a pain type, the first step out of this predicament is to deepen the energy pulsation, which happens most easily through deepening the breathing. Inevitably, this will bring the person in touch with painful feelings. If these hurt feelings can be accepted and embraced, deep crying and convulsive sobbing are likely to follow, tension will be released, and the body will slowly become more alive again.

When this pain has been re-experienced and the body starts to pulsate normally, the pain type discovers an immense capacity for pleasure, sensuousness and joy. Very often, the dulling quality of blocked pain makes it difficult or impossible to allow the intense pleasure of orgasm. Freeing the pain opens the capacity for orgasmic pleasure.

Three Types of Breath

As a way of illustrating the feeling pairs and how they function, I sometimes lead group participants and trainees through an exercise involving three types of breathing, each one related to a specific feeling.

I begin with the in-breath, which mirrors the in-stroke pulsation of fear.

First, I ask everyone to stand in a circle, so we can not only experience what is happening inside ourselves but also watch others.

I instruct them to breathe out, all the way, and at the same time hollow the chest, hunching the shoulders forward and down. This imitates the collapsed, low energy condition of a fear type.

Then I invite them to breathe in with a sudden, sharp inhale through the mouth, drawing the air quickly into the throat and chest, making a gasping sound, while at the same time opening the eyes wide as if in fear.

I also suggest that people imagine the air is entering not only through the mouth but also through the eyes, because this makes it easier to feel the fear. In addition, the hands and arms pull back on the in-breath, so that the whole body seems to reel backwards in shock and surprise.

We do this together, breathing deeper and deeper on the in-breath, with longer and longer gasps, while relaxing on the out-breath so the air is exhaled in a more normal way.

In this introductory exercise, we don't have time to penetrate to the deep-seated armoring of fear around the core, but the breathing quickly builds up a charge of energy and pretty soon people start to experience tension at the back of the neck, which is related to holding back fear.

Later on in the workshop, participants will become more familiar with this form of breathing.

Then I invite them to stop, shake out the tension, and move to the out-stroke of the breathing pulsation, which connects with anger.

I demonstrate what an 'anger chest' looks like by taking a deep in-breath and holding it, puffing out my rib cage and squaring my shoulders, rather like a cartoon caricature of an enraged army colonel.

I invite everyone to copy me and to stand for a few moments in this puffed-up position, holding the in-breath at maximum capacity and sticking out the chest.

What needs to happen now is to breathe out suddenly and forcefully, throwing the air out. It's a sharp exhale, very fast and powerful, with the mouth wide open and the jaw thrust aggressively forward…"Huh!"

At the same time, I suggest that people scowl fiercely, knitting the eyebrows together, and looking as if they could shoot darts from their eyes across the room. As the air rushes out, we also shoot our arms forward, as if throwing the air and energy away from us.

Repeating this breathing pattern, I encourage everyone to make eye contact with a person across the circle and throw the energy out towards them, getting the feeling of a total exhale of the chest.

This starts to open the outward stroke of the pulsation. With anger, the energy is on its way out when it gets blocked, so the tension is right there at the periphery of the body, mostly in the face and hands.

Repeatedly throwing out the air – "Huh! Huh! Huh!" – the armoring starts to loosen, and people have the chance to experience a direct expression of anger.

Finally, we work with the pain-pleasure type. Here, blocking happens on the periphery and also around the core, so the energy is contained within two walls of armoring.

On the in-stroke of the breathing pulsation, energy is not allowed to pass deeper than the diaphragm; on the out-stroke it cannot pass beyond the throat. A kind of rigid compacting happens that numbs the pain.

We need to get the body pulsating, using both the in-breath and out-breath, loosening up a strong habit of control, so I introduce a chaotic form of breathing that is reminiscent of the first stage of Dynamic Meditation.

It is breathing fast and jerkily, in short steps, through the mouth, so that the air pops into the throat, almost like a crazy animal that is panting, grunting and gasping. Sometimes the in-breath is full, sometimes just a short gasp. Sometimes the out-breath is complete, sometimes just a small puff. The body is bouncing up and down, shaking with the chaotic breathing, and the arms go with it.

The general effect is to shake up the holding patterns around the throat and diaphragm.

Then I ask the participants to imagine what sobbing feels like – when you're really crying, as if your heart could break and you can't hold back the sound, so your whole body convulses with sobbing.

A few people slip into real emotion when we do this, but that is not my purpose. I just want to give everyone a taste of the mechanism involved in breaking up the armoring of pain. Laughing does the same thing – it has the same convulsive quality as sobbing – so we end the exercise with laughter.

This concludes the first section of my book, in which I've outlined the main principles of the Reichian approach to restoring a natural state of health and well-being. In the next section, we'll look at how these principles apply in practice.

PART TWO

Taking Off
The Armor

Chapter Six

Preparing the Body

Human beings have been hunter-gatherers for a long time and computer nerds for a very short time. Civilization is a recent development. For thousands of years we were nomads, following herds of wild animals, living so close to nature that we were indistinguishable from it.

In that primitive lifestyle, the body was incredibly important – our primary tool for survival. If you could not run, throw a spear, use a knife, fight off other predatory animals, build a shelter, there was no way to survive.

The women, who did not hunt, also had to be strong: cutting meat, stripping hides, gathering firewood, herbs and fruits, erecting tents, giving birth.... It was a physical existence in which the body was the essential instrument.

Agriculture created a base for a less arduous life, but still the body remained close to the earth, deeply connected to the elements from which it evolved. If you have ever worked on a farm, you will know what I mean. Even with mechanization it is a full-on physical job to tend the animals, sow and reap the crops, keep the equipment maintained and the fences mended.

Modern living is a new phenomenon. If man's history on the planet can be represented by a 24-hour day, it is only in the last few seconds that we see ourselves sliding into the driving seat of an automobile, working in a high rise office block, earning bread by talking into cell phones and typing on a computer keyboard.

The technological revolution has certain side effects and one is that the body plays a far less crucial part in our affairs. We don't need to be physically strong to survive, or even be fit and healthy. We don't need to be in tune with nature or feel a connection between the body and the earth on which it stands.

We want our bodies to look good, especially our facial features and our hair, in order to be attractive to others. Occasionally, too, we have to pay attention to some part when it begins to hurt – like a scratch, a cut, or maybe toothache, headache or stomach ache.

But, aside from these concerns, we can pretty much ignore the body. It is enough to mechanically wash and feed it each day, while focusing on more interesting matters such as the football game on television, the new movie opening downtown, the summer sale at the local department store.

One of my first jobs, when preparing for the process of emotional release and restoring natural pulsation, is to bring people back 'into' the body, regaining awareness of it as an organism, re-experiencing oneself as a feeling, sentient being, re-establishing a connection between the body and the earth.

For this, our legs and feet are particularly important.

Energetically, our legs function as roots into the earth. They are not merely carrying us over the surface of the ground. Just as a tree has roots going into the soil, connecting it to the source of nourishment, so our legs and feet serve as our moving roots, energetically inter-acting with the earth.

When people are connected in this way, I call it a state of being 'grounded.' But, as we have just seen, in today's world we tend to live a very 'ungrounded' existence.

Now teenage girls totter along the sidewalk on huge platform soles and women dance in impossibly high heels. Men and women alike travel to work at fifty miles an hour – feet never touching the ground – and take elevators to the thirtieth floor where they no longer need to run after game to gather food for their families.

As a result, most people's legs are under-charged. They don't have much energy flowing through them. Or, if they do carry a charge – from, say, athletic training or aerobic workouts – there is often a quality of numbness or dullness that comes from taking the legs for granted.

To remedy this, I begin my workshops by inviting the participants to dance barefoot, playing upbeat music with an African flavor, asking people to pay attention to sensations in their legs and feet as they move. I encourage them to stamp their feet, bend their knees and 'get down' into the lower half of the body by dancing, stamping and jumping.

Automatically, this gets the feet exercising and moving in a way that never happens when they are stuffed into leather shoes, or when people dance at a disco or party. Something else starts to happen when the feet are bare.

Dance, in any case, is one of the most valuable all-purpose tools for beginning any process of group dynamics. It wakes people up, gets their energy moving, brings them into the present moment and encourages them to meet and connect with each other.

After a few tunes, I deepen the grounding experience through leading the group into bioenergetic stress positions developed by Alexander Lowen.

Lowen is an interesting man and a disciple of Reich, so it's worth taking a moment to say something about him and his discoveries.

Born in New York City in 1910, Lowen trained as a lawyer but then became interested in the relationship between physical and mental health. He experimented with muscle relaxation techniques and yoga, met Reich in 1940 and began therapy with him, which included not only breathing and body movement but also screaming intensely.

Lowen trained as a medical doctor in order to get a deeper understanding of the relationship between chronic muscular tension and neurotic personality disorders. Then, in 1953, he teamed up with another Reichian physician, John Pierrakos, to develop the body exercises and positions that are now standard techniques in bioenergetics.

Essentially, bioenergetics puts people in uncomfortable stress positions so they can feel the tension inside their bodies, which is released through physical movement and emotional expression.

As you can see, Lowen's work is very close to that of Reich and, indeed, he has credited Reich with providing the basic foundation for his discoveries.

The bioenergetic positions I use for my grounding work are relatively mild – unlike some of Lowen's techniques – but they can still be painful because people are using muscles in an unfamiliar way, putting them under stress, feeling places in the body that usually remain insensitive.

The positions themselves are simple.

First, I gather everyone in a large circle and ask them to stand normally, shoulders relaxed, knees slightly bent, feet flat on the ground and parallel with each other, shoulder width apart.

This is known as 'the grounded stance,' because the body is standing in a relaxed, neutral position, with its weight evenly balanced and supported by both feet.

Then, demonstrating as I speak, I guide everyone to slowly shift all the body's weight onto the left foot, bending the left knee more, sinking down toward the ground, while breathing more deeply than usual.

In this position, standing virtually on one leg, it doesn't take long for the muscles in the left leg to start feeling stress – this is why Lowen calls his techniques 'stress positions.'

The more tension there is in the leg, the more painful it is going to feel. In many cases, the leg starts to shake or tremble, and this is a sign that energy is starting to move and is running up against blocks caused by tension.

Naturally, some people find it more difficult than others to stay in this position, but since I am 54 years old and doing the exercise with them, it's a little difficult for anyone to quit before I do.

Classic bioenergetic technique pushes people deeply into painful positions in order to provoke emotions, but I tend not to work that way. I prefer to do these things playfully, lightly, especially at the beginning of a workshop.

I stay with a single position until just before it creates resistance in people – a feeling of, "Hey, I don't want to do this." In my experience, a relatively soft approach in the beginning supports a willingness in the participants to move deeper, step by step.

So, before the position gets too painful, I guide people back towards the grounded stance, where body weight is evenly distributed on both feet, then slowly shift all the weight onto the right foot, bending the right knee, sinking down and holding the same position.

In this way, we shift the body weight from left to right and back again, maybe three times to each side, so that people can start to feel their legs from inside, feeling the aliveness of their muscles and the energy that wants to flow.

As we move into these grounding techniques, I encourage people to breathe deeply, building up more energy in the body. At the same time, I remind them to keep their attention focused on the area under stress – in this case the legs – because when we combine breathing with focused awareness more energy starts moving in the region where the attention is directed.

Energy follows awareness.

It's an important law of energy dynamics that I first discovered while listening to Osho, when he was describing a series of Tantric meditations that use imagination to move energy to particular areas of the body.

For example, if you imagine that energy is moving up your spine, then, in some mysterious way, your visualization encourages the energy to move in this direction. If you also breathe with the visualization – imagining, for example, that the out-breath is sending energy up your spine, from the sex center to the crown of your head – this will further enhance the flow of energy.

I can't explain why this happens, but it does. It's just one of those pragmatic yet mysterious tools I rely on in my work.

The sequence of warm-up exercises I follow at the beginning of a workshop is not fixed in my mind. I have an in-depth repertoire of exercises, all of which serve the general purpose of bringing people 'into' the body, feeling the muscles, creating a solid connection between the legs, feet and ground.

For example, sometimes I lead participants into the Horse Stance, where we put the feet wider apart, bending the knees and dropping down with the hips as if we are all riding horses, while breathing deeply and feeling the legs in this position.

Or, standing normally, we rock slowly backwards and forwards, without moving the feet, shifting the body weight from the heels to the balls of the feet and back again.

If the atmosphere is serious, I may lead everyone into an exercise called 'jumping like an ape.' Here, the body is bent over in a crouch, arms swinging loosely by the sides, and the knees are also bent. We jump with a heavy hopping movement, using only the lower half of the body, landing with a solid 'thud' on both feet.

I encourage people to scratch their heads, look and behave like apes and make monkey-ish sounds like 'Huh, hoo-hoo, huh!'

In addition to being an effective grounding exercise, this is a good image breaker. If some people are feeling stiff and reluctant to 'lose their cool,' then hopping around the room like an ape and greeting each other with grunts quickly gets rid of the polished façade and brings everyone into the spirit of playful absurdity.

Again, the fact that I'm doing these things with the participants is a great encouragement for them to loosen up and get free of the normal inhibitions of social protocol. If I can behave like an idiot without embarrassment – as if it's the most natural and normal thing in the world to hop around like an ape – so can they.

Once the legs have been given a good work-out and I see that people's energy is more grounded, I shift their attention to the hips and pelvis. This, too, is an important area to prepare for the Reichian work that follows.

Our social conditioning teaches us to stay away from the pelvis because many so-called dangerous impulses and feelings are living there – the most obvious, of course, being our sexuality.

It was not for nothing that the king of rock 'n roll was nicknamed 'Elvis the Pelvis,' nor that, during his first appearance on a major US television network – nationwide on the Ed Sullivan Show – he was allowed to be pictured only from the waist up.

Presley oozed sexual charisma, gyrating his hips as he snarled into the microphone, and the conservative American establishment was worried how this would influence young teenage minds.

Sex is the primary source of our vitality. In the Indian system of chakras, the sex center is the first in a vertical ladder of seven energy centers, reaching from the bottom of the pelvis to the top of the head. The first center operates as a kind of pumping station that distributes energy through the whole system.

Moreover, the first chakra is not just home to our sexuality, it encompasses the physical body and the raw animal energy within us. All of these energies are essential to our well-being and sense of aliveness.

So I invite people to get acquainted with this area by shaking their hips, shaking the butt, feeling their genitals shaking along with everything else. I encourage them to make sounds and enter into a feeling of primal, animal energy.

There is a particularly effective exercise for awakening energy in this area, similar to the one I described in chapter four, where it was used to help people experience a movement of energy through the seven segments.

In that exercise, participants lay down on the mat and began to breathe deeply into the belly, while rocking the pelvis forward and back to generate a wave of energy.

In this warm-up version, I invite people to stand in a circle, feet shoulder width apart, breathing through the mouth, and to use the same rocking movement to stimulate the pelvic region.

On the in-breath, the spine arches and the pelvis pulls back and up. On the out-breath the pelvis drops down and forward in a thrusting motion. So there is a rhythmic swinging or rocking movement with the pelvis, backwards and forwards – the same movement as in making love.

I ask people to 'breathe into the pelvis,' as if each inhaled breath of air can travel all the way down into the hips, and, on the exhale, to make a deep, grunting sound like 'huh,' vibrating this sound in the pelvis.

So we are using breathing, movement, visualization and sound simultaneously to energize the pelvic area.

When everyone has gotten into the swing of it, I add an arm movement, so that on the 'huh' sound the arms shoot forward, as if helping to expel the air and emphasizing the energetic thrust of the hips.

I ask people to make eye contact with another participant on the opposite side of the circle, while we are swinging the pelvis in rhythm together, breathing and chanting in unison, "Huh... huh... huh..."

In this way, people can't help showing their raw, animal energy to each other. I encourage people to enjoy this novel experience, allowing their aliveness and even their sexuality to be seen by another person.

When this is done in a playful, non-serious way it can be a freeing and empowering experience. Any shame or embarrassment surrounding sexuality tends to melt away when the whole group engages in an exercise of this kind.

This brings me to the important and much-debated issue of individual therapy versus group dynamics.

Like Freud, Jung and other founders of psychological schools, Reich worked one-on-one with his clients. Traditional Reichians still continue to work that way, but my mentor, Charles Kelley, broke away from the old school to develop group structures out of Reich's basic principles.

He was not alone. After the Second World War, a whole generation of avant garde psychologists turned towards group dynamics as way of dealing with individual problems on a collective basis.

In 1951, Kurt Lewin, a German-born psychologist conducting research at the Massachusetts Institute of

Technology in Boston, was the first to declare, "it is easier to change individuals formed into a group than to change any of them separately."

Lewin's declaration started a debate among psychologists, psychiatrists and psychotherapists which, even after half a century, has still not been resolved, and I don't think a consensus will ever be reached. But his words opened the gates to a new way of working with people.

The style of group dynamics varied with each pioneer. For example, Fritz Perls, in applying his Gestalt approach to the group context, tended to work one-on-one with each participant, while the rest watched silently.

J.L. Moreno's innovative method of psychodrama, in which participants act out the relevant events in their lives instead of simply talking about them, requires much more interaction between the group's members.

Encounter and marathon groups, which became popular at the Esalen Institute in the Sixties and Seventies, also emphasize interaction – in fact, depend upon it, in order to function.

Kelley created his own personal mix, developing exercises in which everyone could participate, using the group dynamic to awaken energy, then switching to individual sessions for the classical Reichian breathing and movement technique that I described in chapter three.

To me, Reichian work is particularly well suited to groups because even though each individual may regard his or her personal problems as unique, the essential condition of emotional damage and inhibited pulsation is the same for all of us.

We have all been repressed, we all have armoring, and we can all use the same basic principles of breathing and movement to reclaim our energy and restore a healthy pulsation in the body.

In my experience, group dynamics accelerate the pace at which participants can move through the Reichian process, especially in the initial phase of preparing the body and kick-starting energy.

This simple exercise of standing in a circle, making pelvic thrusts while maintaining eye contact with another participant, is a good example.

We all carry shame around our sexuality and we can regard this as a very serious and sensitive problem that might need a long series of sessions with an analyst to resolve. Or we can stand here together, in a courageous yet playful way, making these 'huh!' grunting noises and thrusting our hips in an openly sexual gesture, looking at each other and experiencing the freedom and relaxation of allowing our sexuality to be seen.

I suggest to the group participants that they enjoy this exercise, that they really allow their aliveness to show in their eyes – just to emphasize the feeling of being open about their natural energy. The effect is unmistakable: people trigger each other, spark each other's energy, ride the collective wave, enjoying the game.

Eye contact plays a key role, compelling both people to stay present, connecting energetically in a dynamic way. I use eye contact from the very beginning of my workshops and I will be talking about it in more detail in the following chapter.

Continuing the warm-up series, there is a similar exercise that awakens energy in the chest area, called 'Hands Breathing.'

Here, two people stand facing each other, close together, with elbows bent, the palms of their hands touching. They start to breathe in the same rhythm through open mouths: on the out-breath, the right arm moves forward and the left arm moves back; on the in-breath, the left arm moves forward the right back.

Also on the out-breath, they loudly utter the sound "Ha!" in a way that resonates in the heart and chest region.

Maintaining eye contact, the two partners gradually speed up the breathing, arm movements and sounds. It develops into a vigorous exercise, energizing and opening the chest.

It can be a challenging experience, since some partners tend to be more powerful than others, and I invite everyone to notice if the exercise becomes more of a battle of wills, or more of a synchronized, harmonious love affair between two meeting energies.

Sometimes I govern the pace by asking them to speed up or slow down, and, after five or ten minutes, to stop, thank their partner and find someone new with whom to explore Hands Breathing.

In the course of preparing the body, I spend time introducing the breathing pulsation, as described in chapter two, together with the idea of a hollow tube extending down through the center of the body from the throat to the lower belly.

I also demonstrate the basic breathing position, mentioned in chapter three, where people lie down on their backs on a mat, legs raised and knees bent, with the feet flat on the floor.

Once the participants are comfortable in this position, I take them on a guided exploration of the different areas in the chest and belly where they can breathe. Normally, breathing is so automatic that we never pause to actually feel what parts of the body are involved as the air moves in and out.

I suggest that they breathe all the way down into the belly, into the bottom of the hollow tube, and, as they do so, to gently tap the belly with their fingertips. As I said before, energy follows awareness, so tapping the belly helps people focus attention on the belly and bring energy to the area. It will also make them aware of any tension in the belly muscles.

In this way, we move up the trunk of the body, from the belly to the diaphragm and chest, breathing consciously into these different places.

Many different sensations start to surface when breathing is combined with focusing attention on the body. Participants may feel a sense of constriction, tension, pain, pressure, weight, a sense of being caged, feeling like a wooden block or a stone.

These physical sensations readily translate into emotions.

For example, somebody may start to feel sad for no reason – just starting to breathe and suddenly they feel a trickle of tears on their cheeks. Someone else may feel heaviness around the heart, or maybe tightness in the throat – sensations that happen just before we burst into tears.

Another person may start to feel irritation which, if we stay long enough with the breathing, could develop into anger, or frustration, or a feeling of somehow wanting to break out.

So this tuning-in, which I sometimes call 'basic breathing,' is a way of instructing people in the method that we will be using, the pathway we will be following again and again down into the body.

The final exercise I use to prepare the body for the de-armoring process is very intense and probably the most physically demanding part of my workshops and courses.

I call it the 'Kicking Series.' It requires strong, vigorous movements of the body that include kicking the legs, pounding the arms, shaking the head and twisting the spine – all with the intention of challenging the layers of armoring, shaking up fixed patterns of control that are locked in the body as tension. In a sense, we are throwing the body into chaos so that a more natural order can arise.

For this, I ask people to work in pairs. One, whom I will call 'the client,' lies down with his or her back resting on the mat, in the basic breathing position, and will go through the series first. The other, 'the helper,' sits by the side as a support.

The client begins with ten minutes of deep breathing to build up an energy charge in the body, then I guide them into the first exercise: bouncing the pelvis on the mat – raising the pelvis and banging it down on the mat repeatedly, again and again, while looking at the helper. The mat is thick rubber and foam so they can't hurt themselves.

They do this for a couple of minutes, rest for a few moments, then repeat the pelvic bouncing movement. In rest periods, between exercises, I always encourage clients to make eye contact with their partners, so they can feel grounded in the present moment and resist the temptation to 'space out.'

The second exercise is with kicking. I ask them hold onto the sides of the mat with their hands and kick downwards, stamping their feet into the mat. The legs are raised, the knees come up to the chest and then the feet stamp down in an alternating rhythm – one, two, one, two.

As they kick, I have them turn their heads from side to side and shout, 'No!'

Of course, this triggers feelings in many people because all their lives they have been repressing their 'no.' As children, even as adults, they've tried to be good girls, good guys... nice and polite to everyone around them.

Some people really enjoy the power of expressing a clear and definite 'no,' while for others it has the opposite effect – they can be overwhelmed with helplessness or weakness.

As they're moving the body, it starts to seize up. The instruction is to shake the head from side to side, but sometimes so much tension is triggered that muscles in the neck become completely rigid, so they cannot turn the head. The whole area around the neck and shoulders becomes very tight.

This can bring up feelings of weakness, like 'I can't do it!' and sometimes people just burst into tears. There is nothing wrong with this reaction, because there is no 'right' emotional response to the exercise.

After a few minutes, I ask them to stop, rest, then begin deep breathing again in preparation for the next stage.

I do many different kinds of kicking and movements of the pelvis to get energy flowing and expressing through the legs. There's tremendous power in kicking and we can use it to rediscover how the body naturally supports our emotions.

For example, one stage is to kick straight out, as if kicking somebody off the mat, using language like, "Leave me alone! Get away from me! Fuck off!"

I support each stage with loud music, creating a backdrop of sound that helps people shout and scream uninhibitedly, and also letting them know – when the volume drops – that they can calm down and rest.

The stages are strenuous, but short, with rest periods in between, so anyone who is within the normal range of health can do them.

Then we come to the arms. I ask the clients to make their hands into fists, raise their arms above their heads and bang them down on the mat with as much force as possible, loosening up all those movements we repressed when we wanted to hit and punch someone, but instead held back the energy.

I also encourage people to expose their teeth, because teeth and nails are very aggressive. Of course, civilized people don't rip things apart with teeth and claws but the impulse does arise in us when our anger gets really wild.

I won't describe all the stages of the exercise, but the general purpose is clear: to loosen the patterns of control that keep our emotions in check, patterns that we developed as the process of social conditioning took root inside us.

These patterns limit our capacity to feel and to express ourselves, so the Kicking Series serves the purpose of rattling the cage, shaking things up, throwing the entire system of armoring into chaos. As I said before, it is physically demanding but also very effective.

Usually, I end the series with a full-on 'temper tantrum,' in which, like a furious small child, the whole body is expressing emotion: arms banging, legs kicking, spine twisting and head shaking from side to side.

When the series is complete, we take a break, and then it is the turn of the helpers to go through the exercise, while their partners support them.

In the evening following a day of intense physical exercises, I invite people to share their experiences. Many people feel torn apart, in a kind of chaos inside themselves – both emotionally and energetically – because their patterns of control have been disturbed, shaken up. Some people feel nauseous, others disoriented.

My job is to reassure people that this is a necessary first step in the de-armoring process. It requires a determined effort to break up energy blocks so that the life force can flow freely again, finding new ways of expressing itself.

Chapter Seven

Unmasking the Face

Part One: The Eyes

In ancient Greece, the actors who strode across the stage in those wonderful amphitheaters, carved in stone out of hillsides, always wore masks to represent the characters they were portraying. They spoke through these masks, and the word 'persona' originally meant 'someone speaking through a mask.'

The term traveled down the centuries, mutating as it went. From being a reference to a mask, it was applied to an actor – the term 'dramatis personae' is still used to denote the casting of a play – and then it expanded to an all-inclusive term, meaning any 'person.'

Today, we use the word 'personality' to describe a person's character and it is significant that the original reference was to a mask covering a face, because that is essentially what the personality does.

Personality is the image we present to others and to the world, and the expression of our personality comes mostly through the face. Our image can also be expressed through the body, through the clothes we wear, the car we drive and so on, but primarily, it is the face – its looks, its expressions, its utterances – that conveys the kind of person we are.

In the beginning, in our far-away primordial past, there was no difference between what we felt inside and what was shown on the face. Like everything else that is of the body, the face is part of our animal heritage, and animals express themselves simply and truly, without thought, control, or censorship.

As we became more civilized and started living together in larger social units, cooperation, compromise, developing conventions and taboos tempered our outward expression. We learned how to be phony, how to adapt our behavior in order to get what we needed from the social environment, and this political habit continues today.

So it is not surprising that a great deal of tension accumulates in the muscles of the face, head and neck. We are constantly striving to control the face, to create and maintain the right kind of social mask and keep it in place, showing what is acceptable while hiding the rest.

There are many expressions that indicate the importance of the face in social interaction. In Japan, for example, public embarrassment or humiliation is literally described as 'loss of face' – a phrase which clearly implies the face is a mask that can slip at any moment.

Almost all cultures have expressions like 'a two-faced person,' indicating someone who is untrustworthy, capable of appearing to be sincere while deceiving people.

In America, gambling with playing cards has given us the expression 'keeping a poker face,' which means you don't show any kind of emotion.

For example, you've been playing poker for two hours, losing steadily, when suddenly you're dealt a great hand. You want to smile, laugh, cheer, dance on the table, but you don't show anything – the way you really feel – because you want the other players to bet a lot of money and lose. So your face remains blank.

Similarly, Hollywood movies are full of scenes in which the hero is able to stay cool and keep a 'deadpan' expression in the most extreme circumstances – bluffing the villain and saving an impossible situation.

I've already mentioned the famous British 'stiff upper lip,' which directly refers to a specific area of the face to indicate an unemotional attitude.

It reminds me of an incident that happened just before World War Two, when the British Foreign Secretary, Sir Anthony

Eden, flew to Rome to meet the Italian fascist dictator, Benito Mussolini.

Thinking to impress Eden with his power, the bombastic Mussolini pointed dramatically to a button on his desk and declared loudly, "I have only to push this button to start the next war!"

Eden's expression remained deadpan as he remarked dryly, "How very inconvenient, if you want a cup of tea."

Generally speaking, Italians are more expressive than the British, but this does not mean they have less armoring. Emotion displayed by the Latin temperament may not be a true reflection of what is going on inside the individual, and, if this is the case, the false image that is shown to the world will create as much tension in the muscle segments as showing no emotion at all.

In our own lives, we tend to show one kind of face to our beloved, another to the people at work, another to our children. The face is capable of a multitude of expressions and we learn how to adjust the muscles to present the right expression for the right occasion – it becomes such an ingrained habit we don't even think about it.

The face is where most of our sensory organs are located – eyes, ears, nose, tongue – and where we gather information about the world around us in the form of sight, hearing, smell and taste. This is our boundary, our border, where we inter-face with the periphery, with the outside, and maintain our first line of defense.

Energetically speaking, it is also a doorway through which we can invite the world inside ourselves, or allow another person to become intimate, penetrating our defenses. Here, we determine whether it is safe to open up to others, or whether it is better to remain closed.

As I explained in chapter four, Reich divided the head and face into two segments: the ocular, meaning the eyes, and the oral, the mouth. Between these two, the nose sits almost like a bridge, since its upper half is more connected with the eyes and its lower half with the mouth.

The ocular segment is the first segment to be approached in the de-armoring process and includes muscles around the eyes, forehead and eyebrows, the top, sides, and back of the head, the bridge of the nose and the upper cheeks. It also includes neck muscles that sit just underneath the back of the skull.

This whole area is a channel for energy as it moves in and out of the body, especially through the eyes – it is said that eighty percent of our energy enters and exits via the eyes.

All our feelings can be shown through the eyes, and, similarly, they can be blocked in the eyes. In fact, any place in the body where energy enters or exits is potentially a place where energy can be blocked. The mouth, nose, ears, hands, feet, genitals and anus are other such points.

Children are naturally open and vulnerable to energetic and emotional influences around them. When the child is surrounded by a loving atmosphere, created by caring parents, he takes in – visually and energetically – all these impressions, with eyes wide open and trusting.

However, a child who finds himself in the midst of screaming, fighting parents will unconsciously block this violent energy from entering, especially visually, because no child wants to see this kind of thing happening around him.

Blocking around the eyes often takes the form of myopia, or short-sightedness, which can be a tension-related condition, rooted in fear. My mentor, Charles Kelley, also a teacher of the Bates Method of vision improvement, virtually eliminated his own myopia through releasing eye-muscle tension, and developed techniques that I have included in my own work.

Tense muscles around the eyes contain repressed emotions, and when these feelings are awakened and begin to release, pouring out from the eyes, they bring in their wake a new clarity of seeing.

Seeing clearly involves not only the physical eyes, but also the eyes of understanding and intuition. The physical eyes may function perfectly well, while a state of near blindness can exist at a more subtle energetic or intuitive level.

In therapeutic work, the capacity for 'inner seeing' is important. Without it, all kinds of experiences may occur, all sorts of emotions may be released, but if there is no capacity to perceive their meaning within the context of one's own life, it is almost a wasted exercise. The same old patterns will continue to accumulate tension, again and again.

So in these group situations, or in individual sessions, it's not just a question of going through the exercises. Right from the start, I emphasize understanding why we're doing the things we do. This helps people to develop sensitivity to their own inner radar that tells them what is happening inside.

It's like returning to a state of trust in oneself.

I once heard Osho say that all children are born with 'inner crap detectors.' In other words, they know instinctively when adults are talking nonsense, or doing something inappropriate, and we need to restore this precious quality of directly 'seeing' what is good for us.

Working with the ocular segment is like taking the lid off a pot, which, once loosened, begins to open channels for energy to pass down through the rest of the body.

From here, energy can enter and 'touch' any of the lower segments, just as energy can arise from any center and express itself outwards through the eyes.

In either direction, the eyes are the first point through which energy enters or exits the energy system.

Since the de-armoring sequence works from the top of the body downwards, and from the outermost layers of feeling towards the deeper layers closer to the core, we always begin de-armoring with this segment.

There are a variety of exercises I do to loosen eye muscles and free up patterns of holding and tension located here.

Eye Contact

From the very beginning of a workshop, or a series of individual sessions, while preparing the body for de-armoring, I am bringing people's attention to the eyes.

When I play dance music at the beginning of a group, I ask participants to look at each other as they dance, to see who is here, with whom they will be exploring for the next few days. This is the first step: to connect, in a casual way, dancing and moving together.

When the music is over, I guide participants into basic eye contact, inviting them to stand in front of each other, looking into each other's eyes.

Many people feel shy doing this, because normally we don't look into another person's eyes for more than two or three seconds – any longer is considered impolite or intrusive.

Moreover, avoiding eye contact with another person is a way of avoiding ourselves – avoiding feelings that can easily start to arise when we stand face-to-face. We act as catalysts, triggering each other. The more we look into another person's eyes, the more our own feelings become visible – not only to the other person but also to ourselves.

This can be scary. Our whole effort in repressing emotion is to conceal what we really feel, or to show something phony or fake – something that keeps people at a safe distance – and so, in an exercise like this, it's quite common for people to feel afraid or insecure.

For example, feelings of attraction can start to happen as people realize, "Oh, I like this person." The attraction begins to show in their eyes, but past experience has taught them not to show such feelings. This may come from a fear of being rejected, or from social training and cultural attitudes.

Another thing that becomes apparent in this exercise is that some people just can't do it. They cannot look directly into somebody's eyes. They look at the nose, they look at the eyebrows, over the top of the head...anywhere but eye-to-eye.

Some people avoid by 'spacing out.' They appear to be looking at you, but they disconnect inside themselves and after a while you can see there's nobody home – nobody really looking out at you.

And some people simply close their eyes – they accept that they just can't look.

For those who continue to look, the exercise provokes feelings and emotions. Just to gaze into a person's eyes and see another human being there, looking back at you, is enough for some participants to start to cry.

They are touched in their hearts, because suddenly they feel the common bonds of humanity; that deep down we are all the same – frail, shy, vulnerable. Just this recognition, that "here's another human being looking at me," can unexpectedly touch a lot of feelings.

Changing partners three or four times brings participants closer to each other and this is important in creating a group dynamic for the work that will follow.

Reading this book, you may find such responses out of proportion to the simplicity of the exercise – sometimes even I am amazed when I see how easily layers of protection and phonyness drop away.

But when you think about it, it's not so surprising. It's through the eyes more than any other sense that we meet other people and it takes very little to shake up our defenses when we have the courage to deliberately stand and look at each other. So it's an important and useful step to begin my courses this way.

I continue to encourage eye contact throughout the de-armoring process: expressing emotion through the eyes, showing anger, showing fear, allowing tears and sadness to be seen by the therapist or by the partner with whom a person is working.

Understanding the 'Feeling Pairs' is also helpful when working with the different segments. When I look in the eyes of a client I can usually see the emotion that's being held there. Then it becomes easy to help the client connect with the feeling and express it.

For example, if I see suppressed anger, I know I will need to encourage the outward expression of that energy, emphasizing the out-breath and mirroring the feeling in my own eyes and face. If I see unacknowledged fear, I will show the person how to emphasize the in-breath and open the eyes wider, mimicking an expression of fear, which can then trigger the real feeling.

93

Eye Release

My Pulsation groups are designed in such a way that we sometimes work for a whole day on one particular segment. On the day I call 'Eye Segment Day,' the main structure is a Neo-Reichian exercise called Eye Release.

Before guiding participants into this exercise, I prepare the ground with an unusual meditation technique I learned in India, developed by Osho, called the Mandala Meditation. These two structures, originating in widely different cultures, fit closely together, working on the same energy centers and similar issues.

Mandala is a personal favorite of mine, so it's always a pleasure to introduce it in my workshops and trainings.

I'll begin by describing the meditation technique and then move to the Reichian exercise, because that is the sequence I use.

Mandala lasts one hour and has four stages, each lasting fifteen minutes. The first stage is running in place, on the spot, with a high stepping action that brings the knees and thighs to a horizontal position at the level of the waist. This kind of jogging generates a lot of energy in the lower part of the body, beginning in the legs and feet, then spreading upwards through the Pelvic Segment.

While jogging, people's eyes are open and looking straight ahead, perhaps focused on a dot or mark on the wall, or looking through a window at a tree or shrub in the garden outside.

The combination of running and focusing on a specific point means that two ends of the organism are being worked on simultaneously – feet and eyes – and this creates an energy connection, or unified field, through the whole body.

In the second stage of Mandala, participants sit down, legs crossed, eyes closed, spine straight, and begin to gently sway the body to the accompaniment of soft, ocean-like music. This is a method of centering, helping the awakened energy to accumulate in the core of the body, so that it is not dissipated or fragmented.

In the third stage, people lie down on their backs, open their eyes and begin to move the eyeballs rapidly round and round in a wide circle, allowing their eyes to follow the hands of a large imaginary clock on the ceiling.

The direction is important. This clockwise movement helps the energy to move inwards, and the purpose now is to draw it up to the 'third eye,' located between the two eyebrows.

Most people acquainted with the Eastern system of yoga know about the third eye, or sixth chakra, which is associated with inner sight in the same way that our physical eyes are associated with outer seeing. When the third eye is activated, a sense of inner space is commonly perceived, as well as heightened awareness and mental clarity.

Circular movement of the physical eyes also brings a lot of energy to the ocular segment and this will be useful in the Reichian exercise that follows.

People who are heavily armored around the eyes, holding chronic tension in the muscles of this segment, will sometimes feel sleepy during this stage – some participants actually fall into deep sleep – as a way of avoiding what is being stirred in the unconscious part of the mind.

I counter this by encouraging everyone to keep the eyes moving around, staying alert and present, feeling what is touched by the technique.

In the fourth and final stage, participants remain lying down, closing their eyes and becoming silent and still, doing nothing, just observing or watching any inner sensations and thoughts, or outer sounds. Almost all of Osho's meditations end in stillness and silence.

By the way, if you feel that I have not properly introduced Osho and his approach to meditation in this book, don't be concerned. I will go into more detail at the beginning of the third section, dealing with Tantra and meditation.

After Mandala and a break, participants are ready for the Eye Release exercise.

Here, they work in pairs, one as 'client,' the other as 'helper.' The client lies down in the basic breathing position, back resting on a mat, knees raised, feet flat on the floor. The helper sits on a cushion directly behind the client's head.

The client begins to breathe deeply, building up a charge of energy, while the helper massages his or her head, loosening muscles around the ocular segment, and particularly around the eyes, eyebrows and forehead.

I also suggest the helpers massage the upper part of the back of the neck, at the base of the skull, because tension caused by pulling energy away from the eyes tends to collect here – it's a place where we block fear.

There are many energy meridians or energy channels that begin with the eyes, passing up the forehead, over the top of the head and down the back of the neck. These are usually blocked with chronic tension, cutting the flow of energy between mind and body, and also disrupting the connection between seeing and feeling, so I ask the helpers to massage the neck down into the shoulders.

While the massage is happening and the room is quiet, I explain that there are many things as a child that we don't want to see, we don't want to take in...ugly things, uncomfortable things, scary things, such as our parents fighting, the father beating the mother, unpleasant family situations of all kinds.... We don't want to see those things and so we learn how to cut off the energy in the eyes, not seeing what is in front of our faces.

The Eye Release exercise is designed to loosen patterns of chronic tension that resulted from this protective reflex of cutting energy flow.

I ask the helpers to pick up a small, pen-shaped flashlight and turn it on, holding it about half a meter above the client's nose, shining a small beam of yellow light into the client's eyes.

It is important to move the light in a random way above the face – up and down, side to side, round and round – while the client simply looks at the light and follows it by moving his eyeballs. Only the eyes move, not the head. In this way, the

96

client's eyes are made to look in every corner, every direction, every area within the orb of vision.

The movement needs to be random, not a repetitive pattern that can be followed automatically, as this requires people to remain continuously alert, not knowing in which direction the light will travel next.

Random eye movement touches tensions created around the eyes and also memories that have been pushed into the unconscious part of the mind.

Sometimes people recall images from babyhood: pleasant memories, such as lying in a crib or pram, watching the movements of colorful toys; or uncomfortable memories, when something unpleasant was happening in a certain direction and the baby tried not to look there.

After a while, the clients are asked to follow the light with the nose as well the eyes, so that the head also moves in a random fashion, loosening tensions in the back of the neck.

Through this combination of breathing, watching the light, moving the eyes and head, all kinds of feelings are shaken up inside.

To assist this loosening, I invite people to make sounds, so that the mouth and throat also become energetically involved. I also suggest kicking feet into the mat, which is reminiscent of the running stage in Mandala – knees are bent and feet are kicking: one-two, one-two.

In this way, the legs and feet are generating energy, sending it up through the body with every kick.

This part of the exercise focuses on expression, clearing the energy channels, letting feelings come out as shouting, screaming or laughter, and I encourage this discharge by playing loud, stirring music and guiding the helpers to move the light in an increasingly wild and chaotic fashion.

After about fifteen minutes, I bring the volume down and things get softer and quieter. I ask the helpers to make smoother, slower movements with the light and invite the clients to become more receptive, receiving the light through the eyes.

This opens the doorway for an inward movement of energy, and I suggest that, using their imagination, the clients allow a combination of light and energy to pass down the throat, into the hollow tube and into the heart, belly and sex center.

This receptivity, this inner opening, touches hidden, vulnerable feelings – mostly involving fear and trust – that live deeper down inside us, nearer the core, and sometimes people start to cry deeply.

After about ten minutes, helpers turn off the flashlight, sit by the person's side and slowly bring the exercise to an end by touching an arm or hand, or gently holding the feet to help ground this person, bringing him, or her, back 'into the body' – into the present moment, into a 'normal' state of day-to-day functioning.

Clients then spend a few minutes sharing with their partners what happened during the exercise.

One common experience is that people don't want to see the light, they want to get away from it, perhaps out of a feeling of fear that is being provoked in them. People sometimes feel very angry while looking at the light, wanting to hit out at it, or bite it, or spit at it.

Sometimes the light touches feelings of pain or longing, or, just looking at the light, may suddenly provoke sobbing and crying. Other people experience a feeling of expanded love towards the light – seeing it as something positive and beautiful, and a feeling of wanting to embrace it.

Perhaps, too, the light may represent a mother, father or boss, or some beautiful or evil force, or stimulate feelings of sensuality and aliveness in the body.

With all of these things, the light acts as a projection screen for everyone's personality structure and the conditioning that has been imprinted in this segment since childhood, and many of these personal issues become more visible to each person through the exercise.

In the days following the exercise, people often report seeing more clearly and brightly – things looks more colorful and alive

– and also that it is easier to look into another person's eyes without defenses.

After the sharing session, it's time for a tea or coffee break – a further opportunity to return to the ordinary 'reality' in which we usually function.

People who have been deeply involved in emotional release work are often surprised when, after an intense session, they find they can get up and walk out of the group room with the rest of the participants, to enjoy a tea and snack, before changing roles with their partners and beginning again.

It's something I like to emphasize, not only because I love my morning tea, but because I want people to get accustomed to moving between the polarities of intense emotional release and day-to-day living. It's a good way to keep everyone grounded in the practical side of life, and to not take themselves and their emotions too seriously.

Of course, if someone is feeling particularly shaky or vulnerable, I will guide them to sit in the garden for a while, by themselves, or with their partner, to let everything slowly settle.

By the time both partners have experienced the Eye Release structure a full day in the group room has passed and we are ready for the second stage of unmasking the face.

Chapter Eight

Unmasking the Face

Part Two: Mouth and Throat

The 38th president of the United States was famous for his smile. As candidate for the world's most powerful office, Jimmy Carter knew how to stretch his lips in a pleasing way that proved popular with the public and in the 1976 presidential election he defeated the incumbent, Gerald Ford.

To a nation still reeling from the Watergate scandal that two years earlier had destroyed President Nixon, Jimmy Carter appealed because of his fresh face, clean record and sunny personality.

Alas, the carefree cheerfulness of a candidate rarely accompanies an elected president through his term in office, and White House journalists who took the trouble to count Carter's visible teeth, noted that his smile was gradually shrinking, month by month, crisis by crisis, tooth by tooth.

Rapid price inflation, a Soviet invasion of Afghanistan, the seizing of 52 American hostages during an Islamic revolution in Iran and, to top it all, an attack on the president by a 'killer rabbit' while he was fishing from a small boat near his home in Georgia, wiped the smile off Carter's face.

Now it was candidate Ronald Reagan's turn to chuckle, which he did successfully in a series of television debates with the president, beating Carter at his own game in portraying himself to the voters as a confident, good-humored, sunny man who could give America back its self-assurance and national pride.

One of the interesting things about politics is that, while most politicians try to be charming and act in a civilized way, it is really a naked struggle for power in which people are fighting tooth and nail to defeat each other.

The cultivated smile, the outstretched hand, and the words, "Hi, I'm Jimmy Carter, I'm running for president," all help to conceal a raw, primeval battle behind a thin mask of pleasant behavior.

This struggle for power can be traced back, of course, to our animal ancestors and to nature's basic law: survival of the fittest. It's the strongest male who dominates the herd and gets to mate first with the females.

Animals don't smile. They cannot use the mouth for this purpose. On the contrary, they more often use it as a weapon. Wild animals use the mouth for fighting and feeding; actions that require biting, ripping and tearing.

We all know that when a dog wants to attack, or feels the need to defend itself, its lips pull back to show its teeth while the jaw gets ready to bite. The dog may not be feeling aggressive, but, for example, it may be passing through the territory of another dog that is threatening to attack, and this is a way of saying, "I can defend myself and hurt you, so maybe it's better to leave me alone."

In terms of modern politics, I sometimes think how much more authentic it would be if politicians threw away their smiling masks – if only for a few minutes – and gave themselves permission to bark and snarl at each other. This is the real emotion that accompanies a power struggle and it would be refreshing to see politicians in their true light.

Imagine the scene in the British House of Commons at Prime Minister's Question Time:

"Will the Right Honorable Gentleman admit that Her Majesty's Government does nothing but 'Grrrrr! Woof, woof! Arf, arf! Yip, yip! Grrrr!'"

As for the rest of us human beings, in spite of our efforts to deny the beast in us, there are powerful animal feelings contained in the muscles around our mouths, especially connected with biting and snarling.

Occasionally, these feelings break out. For example, boxing has always been an animalistic activity – two grown men beating each other senseless in the name of sport – but in 1997 a new twist was added when heavyweight boxer and former world champion Mike Tyson, looking for a comeback victory over Evander Holyfield, bit a chunk out of his opponent's ear and lost the match on disqualification.

Many children have similar instincts. Before being properly 'tamed' by their parents they often use the mouth in an animalistic way to express their feelings.

I remember, when I was a small child, I went through a phase in which my anger would come out as biting. When I got mad, I would bite my little cousin or my little sister to the extent that my mother – after repeatedly telling me that little girls don't do such things – finally just took hold of my arm and bit it.

I burst into tears and she said, "See? That's what it feels like when you bite somebody."

From then on, I resisted the biting impulse and eventually forgot all about it until, during my training period with the Kelleys, the memory came flooding back.

So there are plenty of emotional issues locked up in the mouth – not only anger, but also pain and fear – that will begin to surface during the de-armoring process.

In this process, whatever artificial smile or superficial charm has been cultivated over the years is likely to be lost, but since most of the people who come to me are not running for public office, this is a small price to pay.

Moreover, they can trust that, after they have gone through de-armoring, they will discover and experience a much more genuine smile, linked to their natural, authentic sources of love, laughter and joy.

As I mentioned in the previous chapter, Reich calls the body's second ring of muscles the 'oral segment.' It includes the mouth, lips, tongue, teeth, jaw, ears, lower half of the nose, and back of the head behind the mouth.

Here, tremendous amounts of energy enter and exit the body. All our sounds and words are expressed through the oral segment. All nourishment is taken in here, or rejected. Breathing also happens through the mouth as well as the nose, especially when we run.

The mouth is where we, as babies, suckled at our mother's breast, where we first experienced deep pleasure – even, according to Reich, a kind of oral orgasm. He also states that if a newborn is not allowed to suck its mother's breast, the resulting tension or holding in the mouth will inhibit its natural capacity for sensual pleasure.

Speaking of pleasure, the mouth, lips and tongue are all involved in kissing during foreplay and love-making, and these parts of the body are important for giving and receiving pleasure in mature sexuality.

In addition, deeper feelings and emotions that arise from the heart and belly pass through this segment in order to find expression. So the mouth is very active in expressing feelings and, as is the case with any segment through which a lot of energy passes, a great deal of blocking and tension can also happen here.

Neo-Reichian breathing is done through an open mouth, and it is here that the first indication of blocking is often seen. A closed mouth cannot take in air, or let out sounds, energy, or emotions, so it is important to remind clients to keep the mouth open while breathing.

At this point I want to briefly mention the nose, which, though an important part of the face, is not a separate segment in itself. It functions very much in connection with the muscles of the ocular and oral segments, and the nasal cavities connect right down through the back of the mouth into the throat.

The nose is not very mobile and cannot be compared to the eyes or mouth as a vehicle of expression, but it does have its own language, revealing hidden feelings that people would rather not expose to public view.

Many people know the expression 'his nose is out of joint,' which means that someone is upset, his pride has been hurt, but he's trying not to show it. The interesting thing is that it shows anyway, with a little twist in the nose – it's really there, in the face, and I'm always amazed to see it.

When it comes to blocking emotional expression, the mouth segment can be seen as an extension of the cervical segment, located in the throat, because they work closely together and I am going to describe the functions of both in this chapter.

I have already given examples of how children react when told by a parent to stop crying or screaming: the throat tries to strangle the rising energy and emotion, swallowing it back down, while the mouth shuts tight so that nothing can escape into the outside world.

The cervical segment is Reich's third segment and includes the throat, back and sides of the neck, the larynx and the root of the tongue. All vocal sounds originate here, and can be blocked by muscle contractions that prevent energy from moving up and out of the mouth. This segment can also prevent us from receiving energy from outside.

It is through the neck and throat that our head is connected to our body. Literally, the mind and body meet at this point, and phrases like 'keep your head on,' and 'to have your head screwed on the right way' both indicate a need to stay in control of oneself.

Here in the third segment, more than in any other, the three basic emotions – anger, fear, and pain – are clearly visible and identified. The muscles are easily accessible for hands-on work and, for me, this makes the throat one of the most interesting and complex areas of tension in the whole body. It's really a very clear and precise roadmap to repressed emotion.

For this reason, before describing group exercises I use for release work, I'd like to say a bit about how feelings are held in the throat and how they can be released in individual sessions.

Anger is held in muscles that begin under the ear, directly behind the jaw, and extend down the sides of the neck, attaching to the center of the collarbone – the sternocleidomastoid muscles. When we become angry but try to block the rising emotion, these muscles stand out visibly like ropes, tense and hard, as we get ready to explode or fight.

When the therapist applies direct pressure or massaging action with his hands on these muscles, anger is likely to emerge. Simultaneously, the client turns his head from side to side, saying 'no,' and this helps anger to release.

Many people who block anger do so by keeping their voices soft and unexpressive, so making angry sounds and shouting words helps to release this emotion from the larynx. Roaring and snarling like a wild animal is very effective. Sticking out the tongue while breathing out and making sounds helps to loosen anger held in the upper throat.

Fear in the cervical segment is held at the back of the neck and the back of the throat. To connect with this emotion, I ask clients to emphasize the in-breath, opening the eyes and mouth wide. Encouraging the voice toward higher sounds on the out-breath, like a high-pitched "eeee!" scream, also helps to contact and release fear.

You can experience a fear contraction quite easily if you imagine someone sneaking up behind you with the intention to hit you on the back of the head. Immediately, your shoulders come up and your head pulls back as a reflex to protect this vulnerable spot.

It's a place where we feel helpless. Many animals, like cats and dogs, pick up their young with their mouths at this point because the baby cannot do anything to resist.

In humans, chronic tension held in the back of the neck causes the muscles to shorten into a tight bunch, pulling the head back and the shoulders up in a habitual position of defense. However, in most cases, a therapist's hands can penetrate these muscles, loosening tension, releasing fear.

Pain is held in the front of the throat in a sheath of muscles that runs upwards from the collarbone to underneath the jaw. This is where tears have been swallowed, where words of grief and sadness have remained unsaid.

106

A therapist can massage these muscles while encouraging a deep breathing pulsation and inviting sounds. On an energy level, I often find that passing a hand upwards across the throat, without actually touching the skin, moves energy in the direction of release.

At first, when blocked pain starts to release, it may express itself as a kind of whimpering or whining that goes on and on, but doesn't lead to full discharge. In such cases, I need to help the client speed up and deepen the breathing pulsation, opening the mouth wide and intensifying sounds to break the stuck energetic pattern.

Inviting a client to say words directly to a person who was, at some moment in the past, the cause of painful feelings, can also help to trigger a flood of tears and a full discharge of energy.

Exercises for Mouth and Throat

In the Pulsation group process there is a day when my primary focus is working with the mouth and throat. There are many exercises that can be used to loosen armor in these two segments, some of which I use as warm-ups for deeper work that follows.

For example, standing with the group participants in a circle, we can begin to mobilize energy in the oral segment by making faces, bringing awareness to tensions around the mouth. Stretching the face in a continuous series of exaggerated and strange expressions is an effective and enjoyable way to loosen mouth muscles.

Sticking out the tongue while looking at others not only loosens tension held there, but also challenges our social protocol and conditioning that says, "we grown-ups don't do that sort of thing."

Inviting everyone to growl and snarl helps to provoke anger held in the teeth and jaw. As with the individual session, saying angry words with feeling and energy can loosen emotions that have been suppressed for years.

Speaking gibberish rapidly and loudly, in any nonsense language, is an effective way of loosening the oral and throat segments, especially the voice. Gibberish derives from Sufi schools of mysticism and particularly from one strange mystic, Jabbar, who spoke to his followers and visitors only in sounds, not words.

One of the meditation techniques developed by Osho uses gibberish extensively and is designed to unload mental garbage that clogs the mind, paving the way for silence to follow. Called 'No Mind Meditation,' it comprises one hour of gibberish, followed by one hour of silent sitting, every day for seven days.

In Pulsation groups we use the gibberish technique with a slightly different aim: our purpose is to loosen the muscles around the mouth and jaw, open the voice and promote energy flow through the mouth and throat.

It is a shorter version of the process: 10-15 minutes of gibberish to throw everything out, followed by 10-15 minutes sitting silently, witnessing the peaceful, empty space inside which is left in the wake of the departed chaos.

In connection with de-armoring the mouth and throat, I use a bio-energetic stress position called the 'Throat Stretch,' originally devised by Alexander Lowen.

Participants sit on a mat, leaning back, with their hands placed behind the body to support their weight. Feet are flat on the floor and the knees are bent. When everyone is ready, I invite people to lean all the way back, dropping the head back, opening the mouth and breathing.

The whole spine is bent backwards and the back is arched, which expands the chest and stretches the front of the throat, further loosening tension held in this part of the cervical segment.

Participants breathe like this for a few minutes, then bring the body slowly upright and forwards, dropping the head down between knees that are spread apart, so the back of the neck is stretched, provoking feelings and emotions held in this area.

We do this three times, backwards and forwards, bringing participants' attention to the throat area, loosening tension and increasing energy flow up and down the spine.

I ask them not to push themselves, not to force any emotions, but rather just let this position open the body, in preparation for the main group exercise: 'Throat Release.'

Before moving into this very powerful exercise, there is one more warm-up exercise called 'Face Mirroring' which is one of my favorites.

Two people sit facing each other, close but not touching, maintaining eye contact. They decide who is Partner A and who Partner B.

Through a short fantasy trip that I describe over the microphone, Partner A is 'guided' into his own private bathroom where he is suddenly overcome by the urge to make strange faces in a mirror, stretching his face into every possible contortion, accompanied by sounds and gestures.

Partner B *is* the bathroom mirror and copies these faces, reflecting Partner A back to himself, and before long everyone in the room is loose as a goose, acting about three years old.

This deceptively silly exercise is one of the most powerful for loosening the muscles of the face. Its very non-seriousness invites people to make extreme facial expressions and sounds they would never normally allow themselves to do, and this in turn mobilizes the muscles, allowing energy flow.

After about five minutes the partners change roles and go through the game again.

Then we are ready for the Throat Release exercise, sometimes known in Primal Therapy circles as 'Dribbling.'

The two partners remain facing each other, sitting in the same position, breathing deeply while letting their mouths hang wide open, and allowing the tongue to be loose, almost hanging out.

It is interesting to observe the tongue when working with the mouth, because it is a powerful muscle that is actively involved in the expression and repression of any emotion moving through this segment.

Swallowing the tongue is a common method of repression; letting it hang out is an effective way of loosening its habit of control. Tennis champion Pete Sampras was famous for letting his tongue hang out during long, grueling battles on court, and this helped him stay relaxed amid the acute stress of world class competition and perform at his optimum.

The main instruction for Throat Release is not to close the mouth or swallow. Of course, not swallowing, saliva starts to dribble from the mouth. In the neater version of this exercise, boxes of tissues are distributed so participants can wipe away the saliva as it comes from the mouth.

But wiping is also a form of control and an attempt to remain civilized, so in the stronger version I don't allow it. Instead, towels or sheets are laid on the knees and floor to catch the saliva as it falls from the mouth.

Building a charge of energy with the breathing, keeping the mouth hanging open, allowing sounds, allowing the dribbling... pretty soon, feelings start to arise, especially those associated with choking back emotions.

Now nothing is to be prevented, everything is allowed.

Tears of relief may start to emerge, because participants don't have to swallow them down any more. Some people will scream in fear, others may roar in anger.

Each partner may be feeling a different emotion and that's okay. They're just acting as projection screens, triggering each other.

For example, one person may have a dead, expressionless face. This tends to happen when a building charge of energy starts to hit against armored muscles and the pattern of control gets tighter – the whole face becomes mask-like, the eyes look glassy and the breathing diminishes.

This, in turn, may provoke the other partner to greater expression, as he or she reacts to this vision of deadness.

Many people are surprised by what pops out of them during the exercise. All those things they've been swallowing down for years – maybe disgust, maybe the feeling of being forced to eat things they didn't want – creates an energetic reaction of "I

110

don't want it!" Now they can spit it out, or, in some cases, even vomit it out.

I don't push anyone into emotional expression. This is not a 'doing' exercise. On the contrary, I tell participants the only thing they have to do is not prevent anything from being expressed. Nevertheless, powerful emotions are provoked and begin to release.

Meanwhile, my assistants and I move around the room, encouraging the process, sometimes massaging jaw muscles with our hands, or the muscles at the back and sides of the neck.

Personally, I do a lot of work with the position of the head, which is directly connected with tension in the neck and throat. Sometimes it is locked in a forward position, sometimes rotated back – both angles created by chronic muscle armoring.

I wouldn't really call it massage. I'm working with my hands, challenging the holding pattern. At a certain point in the exercise, if the head is held back with the neck contracted, I may pull the head forward and suddenly the repressed emotion will release express itself through the eyes or mouth.

In the same way, if the head position is locked forward to prevent the expression of anger by keeping it in the throat, I may rotate the head back and, as soon as I hit the right angle, the held emotion will leap out of the mouth.

It's not always easy to hit the right point where a client suddenly lets go and the feeling erupts.

I generally go around encouraging people: "Just let it come out of your eyes…let your tongue come out…keep breathing… keep allowing…."

All kinds of things pour out of them, because for years they've been swallowing down so much stuff. They vomit it up emotionally and sometimes they also vomit up their lunch – actually, I try to do this exercise before lunch, but anyway, vomiting often happens.

We stay with this stage of the exercise for the best part of an hour, looking and breathing, not swallowing, and during this time I play provocative music in the background – a driving beat or rhythm that encourages expression.

Then I shift to quieter, calmer music and suggest to the participants to let their mood soften, relaxing more, breathing more quietly, keeping the same position while feeling what is happening inside.

As the mood changes, anger tends to disappear and a layer of tears, or a layer of sadness, is contacted – something quieter, something softer which needs a gentler space to be expressed.

It isn't necessarily the case that noisy, expressive emotion is more significant than quieter, subtler feelings.

This is one of the things I emphasize in Pulsation trainings, when I'm teaching people how to work, because often they have the idea – especially in the beginning – that it's a question of getting clients to make a lot of noise, kicking and pounding on the mat.

For sure, it looks and sounds like a big deal, but it can also be a defense or a performance, a way of pleasing the therapist or concealing more scary, vulnerable feelings.

As a way of ending the Throat Release exercise, I invite partners to come closer and connect their hands. Some move into a kind of energy dance with their hands together, moving to the music, other people start to cry, while others stay with the looking, still not swallowing – by now they have piles of paper tissues next to them.

Then I invite them to hug the partner, if they feel like it, and at this point many people start to cry, because they've been through a lot together, exposing things that have been kept hidden or repressed, they've shown a face that has never been revealed to anyone.

When they come close, their hearts begin to meet, and this can trigger still more emotion. It is a touching moment. Maybe a memory surfaces of how much they wanted their mother to hold them tight…things like that.

Then I invite them to share. I suggest they let themselves be really comfortable, lying down on the mats and pillows, get cozy and talk about what happened during the exercise.

To round off the day's work, I usually play a recording from one of Osho's discourses in which he describes repression, saying it is basically a way to poison ourselves. To celebrate life, he explains, we have to return to a more natural way of expression, so we can reclaim our energy and use it to access higher states of consciousness. Expression is life, repression is suicide.

The combination of these two exercises, Eye Release and Throat Release – one for the ocular segment and one for the oral and cervical segment – creates a powerful opportunity to transform the face, encouraging greater emotional expression, loosening the armoring and throwing off the mask.

As a result, the face comes alive again, capable of showing a wider range of feelings and authentic expression.

Of course, you can still play poker, you can keep a deadpan expression if you need one, but the face itself is no longer dead, no longer in the grip of chronic control patterns.

In addition, you have opened the gate, the entry way into your energy system. You've taken the lid off the pot, so whatever is underneath, further down the segments, can more easily be accessed.

What is inside comes out more easily, and what is outside can penetrate more deeply into the core, because your basic tools of expression – the eyes, mouth and throat – are now more available to help this two-way flow of energy.

This opens the way down to the first major feeling center, the heart, and that is where we will be heading in the next chapter.

Chapter Nine

Freeing the Armored Heart

If we want to experience heaven and hell in a down-to-earth, immediate way, there is no better place to look for it than in the love relationships between men and women. In our efforts to connect and commune with each other, to bridge the gap between our opposing sexes, we discover in ourselves the divine and the demonic.

And, if we want to locate specific areas of the body where the pleasure and pain of this communion are felt most acutely, we must identify two. One is the human heart, the source of love, longing and heartbreak. The other is situated a little lower down, below the belly and above the knees. Together, they do the job.

In this chapter, we will be exploring the heart center, which is surrounded by what Reich calls the thoracic segment – or chest segment – and the powerful emotions this region of the body provokes in us.

One thing that strikes me as significant and often overlooked in matters of the heart, which needs to be recognized by all who venture into this realm: it takes courage to love.

Why? Because when you open your heart you also risk hurting yourself.

Fairy tales and true-love-romance stories have got it all wrong. Love does not last forever. Love comes, loves goes, and when it goes there is bound to be sadness, heartache, grief.

Indeed, we can count ourselves fortunate if this is all we feel, with no added element of bitterness, hatred or regret, for the divorce courts are full of couples who want to tear each other to pieces, squeezing the last dime out of a former lover who has betrayed their hopes and dreams.

As a result of such painful experiences, many people give up on love, shutting the doors of the heart as a form of self-protection.

I remember, during the honeymoon stage of my first big love affair, walking into a post office in San Francisco with my beloved, and going to the counter to mail a couple of envelopes.

I guess we were spending more time looking into each other's eyes than paying attention to the clerk, because she took one look at us and exclaimed, "Oh, you're in love!" Immediately, she held out her two index fingers and made the sign of the cross, as if to ward off evil spirits.

We didn't have time to get into particulars, but clearly she had been wounded in love and didn't want anything more to do with it – and she was no older than her mid-thirties.

It is no accident that in great love stories, like 'Romeo and Juliet,' and 'Tristan and Iseult,' the hero and heroine are never allowed to meet for long. Their love stays pure and beautiful because they don't have time to get tired of each other, hence they never come to the painful endgame of a played-out relationship.

In any real-life love affair, pleasure and pain come as one indivisible package and those brave souls who come to me, to begin the process of de-armoring, soon realize that there is no way to free the heart of its defenses without re-experiencing the pain of loss, hurt and unrequited longing.

This is the price of a return to love and, in my opinion, is well worth paying, for without a feeling, pulsating heart center we cannot really call ourselves human.

In Reich's system of body armoring, the heart is just part of the thoracic segment, which includes the rib cage and all the muscles located in the chest area, from the shoulders down to the bottom of the ribs, in the front and back of the body.

Also included are the arms and hands, in effect making them extensions of the heart. This may seem strange, but we can easily feel this connection whenever we reach out for the love of another human being, or push someone away from us, using the arms as a major vehicle for expressing feelings of the heart.

You may recall that, in my individual session with Erica Kelley, when I first dived into the Reichian work, she invited me to reach out with my arms and say, "I want... I want...." This put me directly in touch with the heartfelt pain of never receiving as much love as I wanted, especially from men, and my fear of asking for it.

In my work as a therapist, I frequently come across similar feelings in my clients. Whenever I guide people into the 'reaching out' movement, either in individual sessions or group work, these kinds of issues are triggered.

So Reich's inclusion of the arms and hands in the heart segment makes sense, especially when we also see them as a means of expressing tenderness and compassion, caring and protection – all qualities related to a loving heart.

Incidentally, you may have noticed – either through personal experience, or through watching movies and television – that the pain of heartache and heartbreak is experienced most acutely in the center of the chest, not in the area where the physical heart is located – more to the left side of the body and below the breasts.

People clasp their hands to the mid-point of the chest when stirred by love or shocked by its sudden departure. Yet still, we call this feeling 'heartache.'

Reich explains this phenomenon as a product of chronic tension held in muscles of the chest, but there is another system that I would like to mention here that also sheds light on the heart and its mysteries.

In the Indian chakra system, there are seven energy centers, beginning at the sex center and ascending through the trunk of the body to the crown of the head.

The word 'chakra' comes from an ancient Indian language, Sanskrit, and means 'wheel' or 'vortex.' A chakra is pure energy – a condensed, dynamic and invisible phenomenon that, when activated, spins like a disk.

117

Even though they have no material form, chakras influence us on a physical, emotional and spiritual level, transmitting and receiving energy, governing the organs closest to them in the body.

I will go into more detail about the chakras in the third section of this book, but one of the reasons why I found it a helpful addition to Reich – and why I mention it now – is that, in this system, the 'heart chakra,' or energy center for the heart, is located exactly in the middle of the chest.

This makes sense to me, explaining why heartfelt emotions are experienced most acutely in this area. It is the energy body that is stirring the emotions, not the physical organ, and the heart chakra is the central point of the energy body governing this area.

Linking the two systems, I like to think of the chakras as the innermost core of each Reichian segment, where feeling and sensation become immaterial, reaching into the subtle bodies.

Yet we cannot dismiss the physical heart as having no influence. I have read excerpts from a remarkable book, titled 'The Heart's Code,' by Dr. Paul Pearsall, in which he claims the heart thinks, feels, remembers, loves, hates, and communicates information.

While interviewing organ transplant patients, Dr. Pearsall found that many of them were experiencing changes in personality and behavior after their operations, and discovered that these new traits actually belonged to the organ donors.

For example, a Spanish boy who did not speak a word of English found himself saying the word 'copathetic' repeatedly, two years after receiving the heart of a man who had died in a car crash.

The wife of the man revealed that 'copathetic' was an invented word used by them to mark the end of a fight – they had crashed in the middle of a heated argument.

In another case, a nine year-old girl received the heart of another young girl who had been murdered, then started having nightmares about being murdered herself.

Her dreams were vivid enough to accurately describe the murderer – she even knew his name. The man was identified and, after investigation, it was found that he had killed the girl who was the donor of the heart.

I cite these examples to demonstrate a truth I have discovered on my own: the human organism is an incredibly subtle and complex phenomenon that cannot be neatly divided into separate compartments: mental, emotional, physical and energetic.

Everything is interconnected. Everything overlaps and intertwines. Moreover, each one of us is unique. Each one of us is a mystery that can never be fully explained or understood.

Any system that is applied to this mystery, whether it is Western in origin, like Reichian work, or Eastern, like the chakras, has its limitations and will be helpful only to a certain degree. Much will depend on the ability of a therapist to tune into a client, using these tools, and then intuitively sense how to adapt and apply them in a particular case.

Another important point to remember, when working with the heart center, is that there is a strong connection between love and sex.

Perhaps this is a good moment to remind ourselves how Reich's investigation of the human organism developed. He saw that Freud's analytic techniques were ineffective in curing people's psychological problems and instead developed body-oriented therapies, based on his own discovery that energy needs to flow freely through the seven segments of the body.

The root of this energy, in his view, is the sexual impulse, so the energy that we experience as love, as an expression of a healthy heart, is dependent on sex energy to fuel its passion.

To Reich, sex and love are indivisible, and here we come up against problems created by our social conditioning, because we have been educated to believe that 'pure love' has nothing to do with sex.

Such beliefs have deep roots in the Western mind and, even though we may consider ourselves 'liberated' and 'modern' in our approach to sex, it is not easy to uproot these attitudes, which have been impressed on us by the collective culture for centuries.

For example, in Europe in the Middle Ages, the myth of 'romantic love,' or 'courtly love,' in which young knights were encouraged to adore unattainable aristocratic ladies, fitted well with the Christian church's ferocious condemnation of sexual pleasure as 'carnal lust' and 'sins of the flesh.'

It was entirely forgotten that the concept of idealized love came from Arabic and Persian literature – most notably, from the mystical poetry of the Sufis – that used earthly love as a metaphor for the yearning of the human soul for union with the divine. Such spiritual themes, imported into Europe by wandering minstrels, lost their allegorical meaning and created an unattainable dream of romance that still haunts Hollywood today.

In the epic of King Arthur and the quest for the Holy Grail – stemming from the same historical period – only one knight of the Round Table, Perceval, was deemed sufficiently 'pure' to go on a quest to find the sacred chalice. Since the Grail symbolizes spiritual fulfillment, the message is clear: 'impure' desires must be renounced to find spiritual salvation.

These misguided ideals, propagated as myth and legend, seeped into the collective unconscious of the European psyche and ruled from there. And, of course, some of the 'puritans' who embraced these ideals eventually found their way across the Atlantic Ocean and set the cultural tone for a whole new nation.

Mutant forms of these old attitudes still appear today in the guise of New Age values and terminology. For example, I occasionally meet group participants or clients who tell me that, in their efforts to adopt a more 'conscious' and 'spiritual' lifestyle, they do their best to avoid 'lower energies' like sex, so that their energy can 'lift up' and be transformed into 'more enlightened' dimensions of consciousness.

The net result of all this emphasis on purity is the castration of the sexual animal within us, and a disconnection from the energy source of love itself. As a result, the heart cannot radiate love because its fuel supply is too low to ignite the flames.

It's my job, or part of it, to get the flame burning again.

Because I emphasize breathing so much in my groups, we are continually working on the chest segment from the very beginning. In a warm-up exercise like Hands Breathing, described in chapter six, the chest area is being stimulated and opened through deep breathing, dynamic hand movements and eye contact between partners.

Even a simple, introductory technique like walking around the room looking into people's eyes, touches the heart and its feelings.

At the same time, sex energy is being awakened through pelvic thrust exercises and later through leg-kicking and pelvic bouncing. So, from day one, the general energy level in the system is being raised and the thoracic segment is being awakened.

However, once some de-armoring has happened in the upper three segments we can start to really work with the holding patterns around the chest, because now the freed energy will have an open avenue of expression through the throat, mouth and eyes.

This is why Reichian practitioners work from the top segments downwards. It is ineffective to attempt to release deep feelings from, say, the belly segment, if they are going to get blocked on their way out of the body at the diaphragm or throat.

As we enter the chest segment, we start to encounter armoring or holding patterns related specifically to hurts and wounds of the heart, to emotional damage that has happened in this area, ranging from mild to severe, from disappointment to devastation.

If a mother dies or leaves the family when a child is two or three years old, such a tragedy is bound to impact the heart in a deep way. But we also carry smaller wounds in this segment, such as not being given sufficient attention by a parent at important moments and consequently developing attitudes of disappointment like, "Mommy doesn't really care about me."

The armoring of the thoracic segment will have different degrees. In the case of mild armoring, feeling is usually accessible once I encourage the client to get the chest breathing in a natural way. In severe armoring cases, I am likely to encounter tremendous muscular rigidity and a vice-like protection in this segment – I can press down on the chest with my hands and it simply does not move.

It is quite common to encounter 'cement-block' chests of this kind, which have acquired heavy armor to hold back pain and rage.

The surprising thing is that such people may be nice, polite and agreeable on the surface. Everybody has this superficial layer, the 'handshake persona,' the social personality that meets with others in day-to-day contact.

When you think about it, it is really amazing how we can manage to keep up this pleasant façade, even when carrying steel-like armor around the chest and heart.

The primary way to open up this segment, whether it is mildly or heavily armored, is through breathing – breathing in, breathing out, restoring the essential pulse of life. This is the key that can unlock, or rather unblock, the tension that prevents us from feeling the heart.

Whether we're working with the emotion of fear, anger, or pain, it is all connected with breathing and especially with the direction of breathing, so I pay close attention to breath-direction when working with this segment.

If I see that fear is being held, I will ask the client to emphasize the in-breath, progressively filling the chest with bigger and bigger inhalations – using a deepening cycle of in-breaths to charge the segment with energy.

Working with anger, I emphasize the exhalation, encouraging the client to repeat cycles of ten or twelve breaths, breathing out as fully as possible.

Feeling blocked pain requires a restoration of the whole pulsation in the chest region, both in-breath and out-breath. Here, the important thing is to keep the chest breathing deeply for a sustained period, because when a person is blocking pain they will often take a few breaths and then stop. By encouraging them to continue breathing I can gradually lead them towards the encaged pain.

The muscles of the thoracic segment are complex, particularly around the shoulders where they connect and overlap with the throat segment. The throat also acts as the expresser or blocker of feelings generated in the thoracic segment.

A lifelong habit of holding fear typically creates a deflated or caved-in type of chest, with tension held in the back of the neck and top of the shoulder blades – the shoulders contract inwards as a protection.

You can try this yourself: contract the back of your neck, so that your head rotates back and up, while pulling your shoulders up and in, and at the same time try to narrow your chest. This is a fear contraction. Tension is created all the way down the back, including the neck and shoulder blades.

Pain, on the other hand, is held in the front part of the body, especially in the pectorals and muscles across the front of the chest. In addition, there's a sheet of muscles, holding pain, which begins at the collarbone and goes up the front of the throat, across the jawbone to the chin, lips and root of the tongue. These muscles are involved in expressing or holding tears, crying, sadness and grief.

Anger, as I have already mentioned, produces an inflated chest – a chest that is filled with air – and the shoulders also become inflated and square, binding muscles at the top of the shoulders. The rib cage is kept in a rigidly expanded formation, unable to relax.

Chests of this type continuously threaten to explode, so the muscles on either side of the neck also become rigid with the effort of holding back anger.

These muscles begin immediately beneath the ears and cross diagonally forward, passing down the neck into the clavicle, or center of the collarbone – where the breastbone of the chest begins. They are involved in turning the head from side to side with a gesture of 'no.'

The same muscles also connect with the jaw, ears, sides of head and temples, so all of these areas are involved in keeping anger packed in.

With so many muscles in the neck, head and arms connected to the chest segment, there are many movements of these parts of the body that can be helpful in releasing emotions held in heart.

I also work with direct pressure on the chest, asking a client to breathe out while pushing down with my hands to emphasize an exhale, while at the same time inviting the person to feel where tension is being held.

It is possible to move the muscles of the whole ribcage on the exhalation, using a kind of vibrating pressure with my fingers on the flat part of the chest, loosening tension.

I can also shake the chest muscles while inviting a client to breathe in, and can press down on the chest during inhalation as a way of making a client put more effort into the in-breath.

Another way to reach the feelings of the heart is to pay attention to the client's hands, because these are expressers and receptors for the thoracic segment.

Through our hands we give and we receive, through them our longing to share heartfelt emotions is eloquently expressed. When making love, for example, we communicate many things while touching and caressing the beloved's body.

Also, hands and arms protect us, adopting defensive positions in front of the body if we want to prevent something or someone from coming close.

Essentially, I am trying to discover the feelings of the client's heart right now, in the present moment, and hand positions are a useful indication. Are they opening? Are they closing into fists? Do they want to strike out? Are they being controlled in some way?

If I see a tentative movement to reach out, I will invite a person to reach up strongly with open hands, saying, "Please come!" or "Don't leave me!" or "I need you!"

If I notice the hands are becoming fists, and that muscles in the arms, shoulders and neck are becoming tighter and tighter, this is a clear indication that anger is being touched. I will ask the person to pound their arms, to make eye contact with me and to shout sounds or words that express their angry feelings.

If the hands come in front of the face and heart in a gesture of protection, fear is being touched. I might work with emphasizing the inhalation which can activate fear held in the chest, eyes and throat.

When the negative emotions have been identified, they can be worked with in ways that I have already described: anger can be forcefully expelled through pounding the arms, shaking the head and shouting, fear can be released through high-pitched screams and tears, pain through deep sobbing.

Once the avenues of expression are clear, positive feelings are able to flow: anger gives way to love, fear dissolves into trust, pain transforms into joy... the heart center starts to pulsate more naturally as its energy expands.

The expansion of the heart is a marvelous thing to see, especially in the wake of deep emotional release, because the outward expression of its energy is like a fountain of love, while the inward expression is an open doorway of trust, and the overall sensation is one of joy and pleasure.

The laughter that spontaneously arises out of the heart on such occasions has a cosmic quality, as if the person who has been through the experience of release can suddenly see the huge cosmic joke in which we human beings are all involved.

Sometimes, when a person is in contact with the heart's love energy, I'll suggest a soft, expressive movement with the arms in front of the chest, beginning near the heart and expanding outwards and upwards in a slow arc, riding on a gentle out-breath, then circling back towards the heart on the in-breath.

This simple gesture expands the heart's energy even further. One gets a sense that the supply of love is limitless, that the heart is connected with a universal source of energy that is capable of flooding the whole world with love.

At such moments, a profound insight – almost a revelation – is possible into the basic cause of difficulty we experience in love affairs and relationships.

The cause is that we look for love in the wrong place. We look for it in others. We get lost in an outward search, a collective syndrome that is reflected in thousands of 'lonely hearts' ads in the personal columns of local papers and magazines all over the world, with appeals like, "Where is my prince? Where is my true love?"

Reichian work has the potential to give people a glimpse of love where it can always be found. When the heart is pulsating naturally, a complete change in gestalt is possible as the realization dawns:

"Love is inside me. It has nothing to do with anybody else. It is my own state of being."

Of course, such an insight is not a cure-all solution. It is not that, from this moment on, we never again fall madly in love with 'Mister Right' – "this time I've really found him!" – or that we never feel jealous when he looks at another woman, never weep when he walks out and slams the door.

But our capacity to sustain the inevitable knocks of love affairs is greatly strengthened by knowing that the other is only a trigger, a catalyst, for feelings that lie within our own hearts, and also by knowing we can connect with these feelings without a lover.

The warm, fuzzy sensations that flood through the heart after deep release work is what we really long for. This is what we want. We lost touch with these feelings because we had to numb ourselves against negative emotions, and now the only road back is to have the courage and willingness to re-experience painful feelings, touching old wounds that need to be exposed and healed.

For me, one of the most beautiful aspects of this work, and one that is particularly apparent when working with the chest segment, is that the body does not, and cannot, lie.

The mind can lie easily. It can pretend all kinds of things, convincing others and even itself: "I'm okay...I'm fine...I'm not an angry person...I love my family...I'm not afraid of anything...no fear..." and so on.

126

But when you come right down to the basic energy system, to the pulsating organism, the damage is obvious to any experienced Reichian therapist. When the chest is held in a particular way, either sticking out in anger, pride or stubbornness, or collapsed inwards in fear, attempts by a client to contradict the physical evidence are not going to be convincing.

This is why Reichian work cannot be developed in the format of do-it-yourself, self-help manuals, because when we try to read our own emotions we can deceive ourselves in many ways.

We can think anger is the main issue, when it is really fear. We can believe we have discharged all the tension in our body armoring, when in fact we are just scratching the surface.

It needs the trained eye of a therapist to read the language of the body and its energy, and translate this into effective action.

Reichian therapy is not for everyone, because it takes people to depths where they will encounter unpleasant emotions and old, disturbing memories. One needs to be interested in uncovering many layers of falsity in order to reach the pot of gold at the end of the rainbow.

It takes guts, it takes courage, to face things that were long ago repressed into the unconscious mind – things that we chose not to feel because it was too painful or too uncomfortable.

For those who do face the challenge, however, it is liberating and rewarding. That's why we do it – in order reach subtleties of feeling and vulnerability, such as the delight of feeling one's own pulsating heart.

And then we can go deeper still....

Chapter Ten

Through The Trapdoor

When you buy your ticket and walk down Main Street into the wonders of Disneyland's magic kingdom in Anaheim, Southern California, you naturally focus your attention on the rides ahead, the costumes of your favorite cartoon characters and the delightful, cheerful scenery.

You tend not to notice the extremely efficient security system, and that's not really surprising because it operates from behind the scenes and underground. It's hidden from public view, coming out into daylight only when required to maintain the 'happy' atmosphere.

It may seem far-fetched, but I sometimes think of the diaphragm like that – as the body's very own personal Disney security system.

The diaphragm is a hidden control center. It's one of those open secrets of the human organism: everybody knows we have a diaphragm, but nobody pays much attention to it, nor spends time wondering what it does, because there's usually more interesting things going on.

When we get stomach ache from eating too many of the wrong things, we certainly become aware of our guts. When we breathe in too much smoke and start coughing, we know all about the lungs and their need for fresh air. When we feel sexy, our attention becomes riveted on the genitals.

But the diaphragm? It just doesn't figure on the landscape of the body, yet it has more control over our emotional expression than any other segment.

The diaphragm is a thin, umbrella-shaped group of muscles that sits just underneath the lungs and is constantly in movement. Each time we breathe in, the diaphragm muscles contract, pulling downwards to make space in the lower part of the lungs for air to come in. Each time we breathe out, the diaphragm swings upwards to evacuate the air.

Breathing is one of those bodily functions that never ceases. It happens automatically and continuously, without a break, from the moment we are born until the moment we die. So the diaphragm is constantly pulsating, constantly moving up and down, and this constant pulsation makes it one of the main transmitters of energy in the body.

I have already explained that one of Reich's basic principles of human health is that energy needs to flow freely through the seven segments, moving like waves, or impulses, through the liquid contents of the body.

In this movement of energy, up and down the entire length of the organism, the diaphragm is a key sector, because here, more than anywhere else, energy can be blocked.

Our breathing is under a certain amount of conscious control. If we want to, we can hold our breath for a limited amount of time, and we do this by clamping or tightening the diaphragm.

You can try this right now. Take in a breath of air and hold it. Feel how you tighten the muscles of the diaphragm to stop the breath. This tightening dramatically diminishes the pulsation that is happening in the body, impeding the flow of energy.

Since energy flow is intimately related to the expression of our feelings, this also means that waves of emotion can be impeded by tightening the diaphragm, so we have the ability to control our feelings from this place – and we do.

The diaphragm lies just above the stomach and the entire digestive tract, so whatever we have swallowed down, in the way of unwanted input from outside – "be nice, smile, say thank you, or we won't take you to the movies!" – has to pass through this energetic doorway and is held down by tension in the diaphragm.

In relation to this, there is an unpleasant but unfortunately quite accurate expression in modern American slang that describes the process of swallowing unwanted things, especially in terms of relating to other people.

It's called 'eating shit,' and usually refers to a situation when someone in authority, such as an employer or boss, is giving you a hard time and you have to politely say, "yes, sir," or "thank you."

Energetically, the throat may be the most active segment when it comes to 'eating shit,' but it is the diaphragm that slams the lid once it has passed through into the lower segments. And it is the diaphragm that keeps it there, because, quite obviously, when you 'eat shit' the natural impulse is to throw it all up again at the first opportunity, and you need a powerful trapdoor to keep it down inside.

A little further down are the belly and sex centers, so, in a way, the diaphragm is like a doorway to the animal energy that's inside us, all the raw emotions that are connected with either babyhood or animalism – the very basics of feeling.

Anytime we want to cut off from these feelings, whether arising from the belly or sex center, the diaphragm is the point where we tighten to prevent contact, pushing the primal impulses back down, forcing them out of sight and out of our awareness.

When we talk about a person having an emotional split, in which one part of the body is expressing and striving for something while the other part is fighting or rejecting the same impulse, this splitting often occurs in the diaphragm.

This is especially true with issues of love and sexuality. The heart, located above the diaphragm, wants one thing, but the sex, located below the diaphragm, may want something entirely different.

For example, you are at an office party, talking to some wickedly good-looking rep from the sales division, when you suddenly realize your sex center is humming and getting turned on.

131

The heart notices these stirrings in the lower regions and says, "Hey, what are you doing? You are in a steady relationship and your sweet, loving, caring, boyfriend comes back next week from his business trip to Shanghai. Surely you can't be thinking of getting involved with this... this corporate Romeo... throwing away true love, just for a meaningless moment of passion?"

Somewhere between the two impulses, the diaphragm struggles to maintain law and order, pushing down your illicit sexual feelings, so you can hold your martini without the glass trembling and carry on talking in an even voice:

"Yes, I did see that movie. I went with Brian, my fiancée. Did I tell you I'm engaged? The wedding is planned for June..."

Another common split occurs between thinking and feeling. The former, of course, happens in the mind, while the latter usually originates in our guts.

For example, after a long pursuit and several expensive dinners, you have finally succeeded in seducing the beautiful young woman of your dreams. Now, after the crowning act of manliness – you're fairly sure she reached orgasm – you are lying by her side in bed.

Suddenly a strange desire arises from deep inside your belly, which, if it is allowed to find expression in words, would say to your partner, "Wouldn't it be nice if I could curl up in your arms like a baby, and lie with my head in your lap while you sing me a lullaby?"

Of course, the conditioned male mind immediately censors this feeling: "Don't be an idiot. You're not a baby. You're a man! She is the one who has to curl up in your strong, capable arms and feel protected and safe."

In many ways, the mind is fighting continuously with our basic needs, and the diaphragm is very much involved.

My mentor, Chuck Kelly, used to say that tension related to internal thought is stored in the diaphragm, and anyone who spends a lot of time thinking, planning, judging and comparing is bound to create chronic tension in this segment. It's another dimension of the diaphragm's role as chief control center.

When you look at the Indian chakra system, the third chakra – the energy center located in the solar plexus, very close to the diaphragm – is traditionally associated with issues like power, evaluation, competition, opposition and cunningness. So Kelley and the chakra system are in accord on this point.

All the three basic negative emotions – fear, anger and pain – are held in check by the diaphragm and the tension this creates manifests as immobility. The muscles are hard and reluctant to move.

However, once the armoring in the upper segments has loosened, I can start to mobilize the diaphragm with the in-breath, on the downward swing, because now a passageway has become accessible, leading into this area. But I can't get there unless the chest and throat are a little bit open – again, that's why we de-armor from the top.

When I'm working with the chest segment, the in-breath is short and sharp, like a gasp of surprise, but when I invite the client to penetrate down into the diaphragm the in-breath becomes deeper and longer.

As the diaphragm swings down, we start to connect with fear, which – as I've mentioned earlier – is held around the core of the energy body, approximately in the area of the physical belly.

The belly becomes involved as soon as the diaphragm allows a downward energy flow and simultaneously the client touches fear.

I see this effect most clearly in very thin women with flat bellies. They are easily recognizable as fear types, having weak muscles on the periphery of the body, and are very light, almost as if they have wings on their feet, or as if their bones are made of a lighter material. One simply wonders where their intestines are stored, because their bellies are so flat.

However, a lot of fear can be stored in a tight belly and this is the first emotion they hit when the diaphragm's trapdoor swings open. It's scary for them. Often, it's connected with a

133

feeling of helplessness, a fear of not being able to deal with some important issue, or not being able to stand up to some powerful figure.

Their whole energy has contracted away from the outside world, into the center, as a means of getting away from whatever threat or danger was experienced.

But this contraction is physically debilitating. When the energy pulls to the center, all you can do is collapse – your legs have no energy to stand, your arms have no strength to defend, and your eyes goes into a state of unseeing disconnection.

This is an extreme case, but I emphasize it to show how the periphery becomes ineffective in fear types, because no energy source is available – all the energy is held around the core.

When we breathe into the belly, allowing energy to penetrate below the diaphragm, fear can be released. Only then arises the possibility of experiencing strength, because the cut-off point in the diaphragm has been keeping us away from vitality stored in the lower part of the torso.

For me, it is exciting to see these thin, fearful women, who have always had to be so nice and sweet, suddenly turn into banshees when the diaphragm releases, their fear dissolves and they connect with the power and anger they've been holding down.

Their rage is stunning, fabulous. This is where women discover the archetype of Kali, the Hindu mother goddess of destruction, who, though feminine and creative, also has the power to destroy the whole world.

When this kind of woman can finally stand on her own feet, her legs grounded and rooted like little pillars, the strength comes pouring through her, together with a flash of anger in the eyes.

It's exciting to have someone stand in the middle of a circle of participants in this state of female power. The woman has just released her fear, and now she's looking at the other participants and saying, "I can show you my strength" – something very simple like that.

It turns her whole energy around and sometimes her whole life as well.

When anger is the emotion being withheld, the diaphragm is frozen in a way that prevents outward expression. With pain, it is immobilized in both directions, in and out, so as not to feel anything.

Add to this the diaphragm's capacity to cut the body in half, splitting the energy in ways that have already been described, and you can see this segment's tremendous importance as a regulator of energy. Combined with the throat, it can effect a total energy shut down, so nothing moves – holding everything in a kind of dead equilibrium.

When trying to mobilize a frozen diaphragm, working with an individual, I am constantly connecting through my hands.

With the out-breath, I press in with my fingertips underneath the ribcage and into the solar plexus region, applying pressure so the lower lungs can expel all the air, then releasing the pressure on the in-breath.

It's not so easy to actively assist an in-breath, but there are ways to put a hand on the belly – actually, between the belly and the diaphragm – and gently pull down, with a little vibration, indicating where the breath can enter, and this invites the diaphragm to breathe deeper.

Sometimes I work with one hand, sometimes with both hands; sometimes on the diaphragm itself and sometimes on either side of the lower ribs.

The diaphragm muscles connect via tissue and ligaments to the inside of the ribcage, and this connection occurs all the way around to the back of the body, where fear is held.

Reich talks a lot about this phenomenon of fear held in the back, saying the body's language in this region gives the impression that somebody is expecting to be hit on the head from behind. It's a product of shock, of sudden surprise... everything seems fine and then "Bang!" The head goes back, the shoulders tense, the spine arches.

Incidentally, this is why we describe a scary movie as 'spine-chilling' – because it touches the fear in our backs.

135

When working with this area, I reach around the body, as it lies on the mattress, and press muscles at the back of the diaphragm with my fingers, while encouraging deep breathing, and this often brings up surprising, unexpected things that have been hidden away.

Issues held in the back are kind of secret – that's why we keep them behind us.

I will be massaging muscles next to the spine in this area, thinking I am dealing with fear, when suddenly anger will pop out – anger that has been buried away, held out of sight.

For example, it may be that a female client has a strong belief that she loves her mother, that her mother has always supported her, protected her from a bad-tempered father and other male relatives. Then suddenly the client's anger erupts, together with a realization that the mother manipulated her out of jealousy, binding her into a suffocating relationship that excluded the love of the father.

As part of diaphragm release work, I invite people to make sounds that vibrate through the muscles of this segment, like "Hoh!" When the diaphragm is open and the sound can vibrate down into the belly it can be a deep roar, or, if the diaphragm is stuck, the sound will be more of a grunt. The same sound vibrates the throat segment and helps expression.

As I said earlier, the diaphragm is involved with many things that we've swallowed down – literally, figuratively and energetically – and particularly with swallowing things that would have made us angry, disgusted, sick to the stomach.

At the time of swallowing, we couldn't permit the natural impulse to throw up, but certain exercises will provoke this. For example, when we do the Kicking Series, or Temper Tantrum, we torque the body, twisting the spine in a particular way that shakes up the diaphragm.

This, in turn, gives a feeling of losing control and one of the feelings associated with loss of control is nausea – as energy which has been swallowed down starts to release.

It often comes with such a force that the person will actually vomit and this is a good thing, because with vomiting comes a powerful emotional discharge. Often rage comes pouring out, along with disgust: "How dare you make me eat my peas?" or "How dare you make me go to school?"

Anything that we've ever been forced to do, that we didn't want to do, surfaces with this nausea and rage as the diaphragm releases.

By now, you will be aware that our emotions can be held, felt and expressed through all the segments. What changes, as we move downwards, is that the emotions come from deeper places in the body, with a parallel deepening of intensity.

For instance, if a client starts to cry at the beginning of a de-armoring process, the energy of tears and crying will be expressed through the eyes, throat, mouth and perhaps a little bit in the chest, so the energy remains in the upper part of the body.

If I look at the client's body, I can see that the energy is not penetrating below the thoracic segment, and the crying will have a high sound, like a kind of whining and complaining. Or it contains a nagging quality, an irritation that would like to become anger but has no power, and could go on like this forever.

As I encourage the client to breathe more deeply, starting to work with the chest, the lungs take deeper breaths and sobs will start to come from the area around the heart, rushing up through the throat to the mouth and the eyes.

Then, if the client stays with the crying, a moment comes when the diaphragm lets go, the energy drops into the lower segments and deep sobs emerge from the belly.

You know the expression 'heart-breaking sobs' and also the expression 'gut-wrenching pain,' or 'gut-wrenching feelings.' These are linguistic indications of how the intensity of emotions increases as we move down the body.

Maybe this is a good moment to talk about my own involvement in a client's process. I've already said that it's gratifying when a group participant or individual client achieves a breakthrough and releases pent-up energy.

137

Similarly, it can be frustrating when a breakthrough is not achieved, but I am more likely to be just curious, wondering, "Where is the key? What will support this person to get in touch with feelings and express them?"

Mostly, I am not invested in whether clients come through with their fear, anger or pain – or with their joy. But I give each session my best shot, trying as many things from my bag of tricks as feels intelligent and appropriate.

Many things I do are spontaneous, pulled out of the moment, using my storehouse of thirty years' experience.

For example, I may be working with touch, breathing and movement, then suddenly feel the need to try a psychological angle. I may ask questions as the client is breathing, or ask if any words can express what is being felt. These words may open up a whole story and I'll encourage that to continue, letting the memories surface and unravel.

Whatever happens, the therapist has to be involved energetically with the client. A session is two people working together. It's not that I am doing something to the client, nor is a client all by himself, just breathing on his own.

It's something we're exploring energetically, together.

I don't register the process of a session in a rational, logical way. I am tuning into different things: picking up tensions with my hands, noticing something about breath direction, feeling energy flow, seeing how the body is moving, listening to the sounds being expressed....

Sometimes, I experience a reflection in my own body of what is stuck in a client. I tune into my body while I'm working and feel exactly where the energy is being held – maybe in the core of the throat, maybe somewhere in the chest, maybe somewhere deep, deep inside.

With this intuitive feeling, I can suggest making a sound that vibrates this area in the client's own body, or to move and breathe in a way that touches or shakes up the place where energy is being held.

When they get it right, when they've found the spot, I say, "Yes, that! Let that happen!" It's important to let clients know

138

when they're on the right track. I affirm it, support it, acknowledge it, so they can go deeper into that place, so the emotion can be contacted and triggered.

I enjoy a good release, for the simple reason that I love to experience strong energy moving. I love a good thunderstorm, I love a good orgasm, I love a good expression of rage.

I also love the quiet after the storm, when the energy has calmed down. This calm is not a dead type of quietness, like a graveyard, but silently alive, pulsating and yet restful. This space, after a full release, is as valuable as the release itself, because this is the time when energy floods back through the whole system.

The places that were tense before are now relaxed enough to absorb a new quality of aliveness. At the deepest level, the whole energy can turn inwards and create a silent moment of meditation and self-contact that was not available before.

The client was trapped on the surface by his own armoring until the muscular tension had released and then...'Whooom!' He drops to the center.

My job is to support this delicate new space, either by inviting the person to close his eyes, resting his hands on his own heart or belly, or by inviting eye contact with other group participants, silently sharing what is being felt inside.

This can be a very moving experience, when a person looks up and sees the people around him, because many of them are also feeling the joy that is bubbling up. It's a kind of synchronicity. It's liberating for the whole group, because everybody can get on the same train, everybody can ride the wave of energy created by one person's release work.

Well, almost everybody. Some people hate it. They cut off and go away from the group into a corner, or to the bathroom, because the feeling that has been released is now vibrating something inside themselves that they have rejected. And this is the signal that it's time for them to look at a particular issue and go deeper.

Chapter Eleven

Into The Depths

The belly is the next step inwards or downwards in the de-armoring process.

From here, feelings arise.

From here, impulses of energy begin.

The upper segments may be the expressers of those feelings and impulses, but the belly is the origin. Similarly, the upper segments can be receptors for impressions entering from outside, but it is the belly that responds.

Whatever we are feeling, whether pain, disgust, rejection, fear, anger... these feelings have their source in the belly.

In Western countries, people have been trained to be more head-oriented and so the idea of the belly as a seat of feeling may at first seem strange.

For example, when a feeling of disgust arises, we may think this originates in the mind, while an expression of disgust may appear to go no deeper than the mouth, as it curls up in disapproval, or perhaps the throat, as appropriate sounds emerge to register distaste.

In traditional Chinese and Japanese cultures, however, the belly has long been regarded as the seat of psychological and emotional well-being. This is especially true of the hara, located in the lower belly, approximately three finger widths below the navel, which is considered to be the source of life energy.

The Indian chakra system locates the second chakra in the lower belly, close to the hara, and gives it control over social interaction, group energy and companionship, as well as over emotions and feelings.

The second chakra builds upon the first like two rungs in an ascending ladder of human needs. The first chakra takes care of essential, basic survival needs – food, shelter and sex – and only when these are met is there a possibility of enjoying social interaction for its own sake, including tribal and family life, and the accompanying emotional atmosphere.

When viewed from these perspectives, it is clear that the Western habit of giving the head so much predominance is an acquired cultural and regional attitude. In reality, as I mentioned earlier, the processes of thinking and feeling are spread throughout the entire body.

When we approach the belly as part of the Reichian de-armoring process we are continuing something that began earlier. From day one of any workshop or training, as soon as I introduce the basic breathing position, we start breathing into the belly in order to tap into the vitality and aliveness which lies in the lower segments.

So belly breathing happens right from the start. However, as we saw in the last chapter, natural belly breathing involves the pulsation of the diaphragm, which needs to be able to swing down easily on the in-breath and up on the out-breath.

People whose diaphragm is not able to pulsate freely in this way have difficulty breathing into the belly. When I ask a client to do this at the beginning of a course, I'm aware that it will have only a limited effect, and that a lot of loosening and opening will be needed in the upper segments before real belly breathing can happen.

When these upper segments are loosened and the diaphragm becomes mobilized, we can enter into deeper layers of feeling, accessing the pool of emotion that lives in the belly, which is one of the body's two main feeling centers – the other being the heart.

The belly is the place where, before birth, we connected with the mother through an umbilical cord, and so all of those primal 'baby-mother' feelings like need and fulfillment, nourishment and sustenance – feelings that began with the fetus and carried into early childhood – are found here.

Given the primitive, pre-linguistic nature of such feelings, it is natural that they are buried underneath many experiences that came afterwards, layer upon layer, pushing our primal emotions down into the unconscious.

Because of this, the belly has an air of unconsciousness surrounding it, an atmosphere of something not known, of things buried deep, including some of our oldest and earliest wounds – especially those relating to fear.

I have already explained how the flat belly of thin women is connected with fear held close to the core of the energy body. Any kind of work with the belly is likely to touch this layer of fear, plus a whole range of related feelings such as helplessness, collapse, wanting to run away, wanting to be gone, wanting to not remain here a moment longer.

Sometimes people literally disappear into the belly when these feelings are touched. They cannot escape outwards, so instead their attention goes deep inside and this becomes a way of cutting off from whatever fears have been awakened.

This was learned in childhood as a survival strategy and is the human equivalent of the proverbial ostrich sticking its head in the sand so as not to see danger approaching.

I can't imagine that ostriches really do this, because in the wild it would simply mean death. But as a metaphor for certain types of human behavior, the image works well, particularly for a helpless child who cannot escape from an angry or abusive parent – the only way out is to disappear inwards.

One of the strongest emotions that is likely to be encountered in the belly region is fear. This fearful contraction has to be approached delicately, because it may be rooted in shock and a vigorous approach will only re-traumatize or strengthen the original experience of shock.

Usually, I emphasize deep in-breaths into the belly to penetrate the core, while maintaining eye contact and gently resting my hand on areas of the belly that feel hard or tense.

Often, I will not actually touch the physical belly, but keep my hand an inch or two above the skin, connecting with the energy body.

143

Here, the energy body is easily accessed, because the physical body is comparatively soft and fluid. The belly has no bone structures, joints or ligaments, only a wall of muscle that holds in the intestines and their continuously moving contents.

Tension held in the muscles of the upper body tends to be specific in its location, such as the jaw, the side of the throat, and so on, whereas in the abdomen, tension exists more as an amorphous mass.

In this situation, direct pressure on muscles with fingers and hands is not likely to be as effective as energy work, especially when working with fear.

I may move my hand slowly, or perhaps quickly, without touching the belly, and energy emanating from my hand stirs and stimulates the energy body of the client. This in turn connects with emotion locked in the muscles.

If the emotion is fear, the main thing a client needs to do at this point is to *not* go away, to *not* escape, but instead to remain in touch with the feeling that has been contacted. Here, courage and awareness are needed, because the instinctive reaction is to disappear, either inwards or outwards.

Once fear has been felt and released, a doorway is open for anger to rush out, which it often does in dramatic fashion.

In the previous chapter, I talked about control issues in relation to the diaphragm, and these kinds of issues continue into the belly, especially related to early experiences of force or compulsion, like toilet training, having to eat at certain times, having *not* to eat at other times, and dressing in certain ways.

Compulsion might include such commands as:
"You have to go to the bathroom now."
"You have to eat now."
"You have to go to bed now."
You can imagine what kind of rage can start to emerge, when the fear that has been blocking the child's natural responses is released and permission is given to express authentic reaction to such commands.

For example, a child who lives in a life-threatening situation, such as having a father who is routinely violent or drunk, is

144

unable to show any kind of rage or anger because that would have provoked even more abuse.

Such emotions have to be packed down, right down into the belly, where they lie hidden for years. When this person is finally given permission to connect with, and release, these long-forgotten feelings they often discover a murderous rage towards the parent who abused them.

"I could kill you!" is the kind of emotion that comes up from the belly.

These deep-seated feelings are not contacted immediately, at the beginning of a session. What usually happens is that a client begins to move into emotional release in the upper part of the body, especially in the chest, then, as the diaphragm opens, the expression deepens until the emotion comes from the level of the belly, right out of the guts, with tremendous power.

As guide and therapist, I follow what is coming layer by layer, segment by segment, and this is not always a one-way direction. Sometimes, after working down through the segments to the belly, the released energy and emotion will rise up through the diaphragm but become held in the chest or throat.

I need to bring my attention again to the upper part of the body, working to release tension in the affected segment before returning to the belly once more. I keep rooting back down to the belly because I am inviting the feeling to come from as deep a place as possible – this is my constant orientation.

After any kind of release, of any kind of emotion, a relaxation phase is bound to follow, a natural cycle enshrined by Reich in his orgasm formula – charge, tension, discharge, relaxation – which I'm using constantly in my work.

In the relaxation phase, I invite the person to close his eyes and breathe slowly and deeply into the belly, also connecting with the legs, keeping his attention in the lower segments, recharging the belly area. Then, after a few minutes, another wave of emotion may arise and be released through the upper segments.

145

There comes a point, after a client has experienced many sessions, when a clear channel is open all the way down to the belly and he, or she, is able to work consistently from depth.

Typically, this happens towards the end of a course, when clients are able to connect with, and accept, what lies in the deepest parts of themselves, including things they have not wanted to see during their whole adult lives: gut-wrenching sadness, grief or pain, maybe a tremendous loss as a child, such as loss of a mother at the age of three or four years old.

I remember feeling a similar kind of pain when my family moved house. I had been so in love with my little cousin – we were both seven years old and did everything together. Our families lived next door to each other, so we were constant companions.

Then my parents moved to another state, about nine hours away, and this completely disrupted our connection. From then on, we saw each other only once a year.

For months, I felt a deep sadness, and I know that I just buried it, buried it again and kept on burying it until eventually it vanished out of sight.

It is these kinds of feelings – emotional loss, depths of rage, shattering disillusionment – that are held around the belly and the energetic core.

It's possible to encounter the same issues while working with upper segments. Many times, psychologically or emotionally, we may come across a particular traumatic incident, but each time, as we work deeper, we come a little closer to the core feeling. Suddenly, as we drop into the belly, we are right in the middle of it, with a full and total connection.

This brings me to an exercise I do in my groups, usually towards the end of the process, called Unfinished Business.

I mention it now because it involves the belly segment. It's very much a 'feeling' exercise and is designed to help people look back into the past and recognize a situation with a specific individual that is incomplete; something that has been ignored and locked away in the unconscious mind; some feeling that has never been expressed or acknowledged.

Because the situation is incomplete we continue carrying it in the form of chronic tension in our body armoring and also as loose bytes of psychological data floating around in the biocomputer of the mind. Unfinished Business works at psychological and emotional levels simultaneously to resolve the situation.

Before guiding participants into the structure, I begin with a couple of warm-up exercises – soft bioenergetics stress positions – designed to help people connect with the belly.

First, I ask them to lie on their backs, on a mat, in the basic breathing position, knees raised, feet flat on the floor, tapping with their fingertips around the belly area to find where they are carrying tension in this segment and help let it go.

Breathing into the belly, I ask them to lift the head off the floor and look directly forward through their own raised knees. Most people use their belly muscles to pull the head up, so the belly immediately gets tight and breathing becomes restricted.

Then I ask them to exhale, letting the head down, noticing, as they do so, how the belly muscles relax. I explain that it is possible to use other muscles, such as those at the back of the neck, to do the work of holding the head up, allowing the belly to remain soft.

I invite them to try again, on their own, for about fifteen or twenty breaths, raising the head and letting it down, experimenting to see if they can keep the belly relaxed. This simple technique gives people a sense of how tensions in the belly are often created unnecessarily.

In another exercise, also beginning in the basic breathing position, I invite participants to take their knees in their hands – right knee in right hand, left knee in left hand – pull the knees up into the chest and let their hips and lower back roll around on the mat. This baby-like position is a playful way of loosening the pelvic and sex area.

Then, keeping the pelvis on the floor, I ask them to lift their legs high into the air so that the soles of their feet are flat and facing the ceiling. In this position, they are pushing the heels up so there is tension in the back of the legs.

It is possible to let the legs float above the body, supported and held by muscles in the hips. But what usually happens is that the lower back muscles are too tight to allow the legs to remain directly above the body, so people have to use their belly muscles to hold them up.

I invite them to explore the position, making fists with their hands and placing them under the buttocks for extra support, and feeling the muscles that are under stress in the belly and the lower back – the abdominal segment includes both areas.

These two exercises bring people's energy and attention into the belly area, and we can then move to the Unfinished Business structure.

The exercise combines the classic Gestalt technique of speaking from both halves of a situation or relationship, together with neo-Reichian breathing, which brings a higher energy charge to the experience.

It requires two people, working as partners, one as client and the other as helper. The client lies on the mat in the basic breathing position, while the helper sits close by.

Clients begin by building up a charge of energy in the body through deep breathing into the belly, and one of the jobs for the helping partner will be to ensure that this deep breathing is maintained throughout the exercise.

Meanwhile, I put on soft music, often with a sad flavor or with a quality of child-like simplicity, to help evoke an appropriate mood.

I ask the clients to close their eyes and then begin to guide them into the past, asking them to look back through the years, remembering some of the people who have been emotionally significant for them, people whom they loved, people who loved them, people with whom they were very close. These are the people we are still carrying inside us – people that we care about, in some way or other.

I ask them to recall a particular situation with one person. It may be a situation involving negative feelings, like resentment or hurt, or positive feelings that were never fully expressed –

maybe someone they loved but never allowed themselves to directly say, "I love you."

It could be a parent, a grandparent, or someone else that was significant when they were young. It could be a brother, sister, cousin, or perhaps someone more recent, like a boyfriend, girlfriend, husband, wife, lover. It could be someone who died, someone they will never see again.

I invite the clients to find this special person, imagining the person is here with them, in the room, right now, to call out the person's name a couple of times, look into their eyes and begin to speak to them, saying whatever was not said before.

Naturally, as this happens, emotions start to arise, and I suggest letting the body move, allowing feelings to come out. But what's very important in this exercise is verbalizing.

Words connect emotions with the mind and this is what we want: a direct communication in a specific situation with another person, so that whatever has been lingering around for years in the mind and body, regarding this issue, can be healed and dissolved.

We may have said these things to ourselves a million times inside the mind, but when we say them out loud we hear and understand them better. In addition, the sounds of the words create vibrations in the body and these vibrations help to bring the unconscious into the conscious.

I ask helpers to give support energetically to the clients by letting their hands move from the belly up the front of the body, not touching the skin but staying a couple of inches above.

As I explained earlier, energy in the helper's hand connects with energy in the belly of the client and this helps to create a kind of 'expression stream,' a flow of energy that moves across the belly, across the heart and over the throat – it can be very helpful in encouraging expression.

Within a few minutes, many participants begin to cry or shout as old wounds are touched and they release what has been long held back. I encourage them to let words come, to keep breathing, to allow the body to assist expression in any way that feels right, including pounding the mat with fists or kicking out with legs and feet.

After about ten minutes, I ask the clients to let the words go, becoming silent, taking a moment to fall inside and rest, and then to notice what this other person is feeling, having heard what has been communicated.

I ask them to imagine becoming this other person, to call out their own names, as if being personally addressed by this person, and to let him or her speak.

Usually, it takes a couple of minutes to get into the swing of being the other person, but most people manage to do it, spending the next ten minutes speaking from that person's viewpoint and feelings.

Maybe I should say here that, before starting, when I explain the exercise, some people object to the idea of role-playing another person, saying things like, "How can I know what my father was thinking then?"

But somehow we do. When we tune in, when we focus on the person, we discover a deep psychic connection and understand what was going on inside him.

Playing the other person as well as addressing him makes the process more round and complete. Otherwise it would be too one-sided, an opportunity to throw out emotions, but not with the same depth of release, not with the same qualities of compassion and healing.

When this stage is finished, I invite the clients to again become themselves, to express whatever else is needed to complete the exchange, and then to feel if they are ready to forgive this person, or to ask forgiveness – whichever feels appropriate.

I encourage them to speak from the heart, to see if they can bring new insights into the relationship that can heal the wound. Then I ask them to find a way to say goodbye to this person and let them go.

Slowly, I bring the clients back into the 'real' world, the present, making contact with their helpers, spending a few minutes sharing the experience, explaining with whom they spoke and what significance this person had in their lives.

Then, after a break, it's time to change roles and do the exercise again.

Reading a description of this exercise, you may think, "Well, I can do it myself, sitting in this chair, just by closing my eyes and thinking of somebody."

The short answer is, yes, you can. And, in fact, Gestalt exercises of this kind are done in counseling sessions all over the world, using two cushions. The client sits on one cushion, imagines a person to be sitting on the other, and starts talking.

This can be very effective, especially with a skilled counselor, but in my experience it does not have the same emotional depth as can be gained through combining Gestalt with Reichian work.

I usually do this exercise on the fifth day of a five-day group process, toward the end of a workshop. By this time, people's bodies have loosened up, their energy is flowing more naturally and they are connected with their emotions.

In this state, to focus on issues of unfinished business with a significant person is bound to be a more profound experience.

Also, entering into the process in a lying down position, with closed eyes, greatly assists regression and vulnerability. You can easily become a baby in a crib, or a child in a cot, especially with someone sitting at your side, taking care.

I have done the exercise without helpers, with all of the group's participants working by themselves, but I have found that the presence of someone who is supporting and listening keeps clients on the right track, making it difficult for them to space out or drift away from the structure.

Moreover, helpers are usually enthralled by what's going on and often become emotionally involved, empathizing and perhaps weeping as they hear a touching story unfold.

Up to now I have talked about the abdominal segment in relation to mother issues, gut feelings, unhealed emotional wounds – negative things held down in the belly – and now it is time to address the positive.

The belly's capacity for pleasure is immense, including, for example, the deep enjoyment of a baby as it sucks at its mother's breast, or is held in her arms, or rests on her body.

Pleasurable sensations of the physical body are felt through the belly center. As I said before, there is a communion between the physical and energy bodies in this segment, so feelings in the physical body easily register in, or vibrate through, the energy body as it inter-penetrates the physical form.

A baby at the breast is totally involved: its lips are sucking, its hands are touching, its stomach is being filled, its whole body is being nourished. All these sensations of taking in nourishment are experienced through the belly, which absorbs the feelings and transmits them to the energy body, which then expands with pleasure, creating an aura of satisfaction surrounding the entire physical body.

The sense of deep relaxation and contentment that follows a baby's feeding session is also an energy body – or second body – experience.

In Reichian work, after an intense session in which clients have been through strong emotional release, they naturally fall into this space of pleasurable relaxation. This is one of those rare moments in adult life when a person can really let go of all tension and anxiety, enjoying a sense of not needing to do anything, a sense that all is well.

When a client has moved into this space, I will gently put his hands on his own belly. This intensifies the experience and gives the feeling of being 'at home,' a sense of oneness, of being in a state of harmony.

The client may have walked into the room in a fragmented state, with all kinds of energy splits. When these conflicting energies have been expressed and released, every segment of the body connects harmoniously to every other part – at least for a while.

What adds to this sensation is a state of free-flowing energy through all the segments. The energy can flow into the fingertips, reach to the heart, get right down into the sex center and all the way to the legs and feet, creating a feeling of wholeness that is somehow perceived through the belly.

It is an organic feeling, a bio-energetic phenomenon, very pleasurable, and not normally accessible for most people. We may experience moments of happiness or excitement in other ways, such as a climactic moment in sport, or the rush of winning at gambling, but these are nowhere near the organismic experience that produces pleasurable core feelings.

However, there is one other type of experience that comes close to giving us this type of pleasure, and that is sex. Making love, reaching orgasm, sharing love, has the capacity to touch the same level of delight, and our ability to enjoy such experiences depends totally on the health and vitality of the pelvic segment, which will be addressed in the following chapter.

Chapter Twelve

Down to the Roots

As far as contemporary Western society is concerned, Sigmund Freud was the revolutionary genius who opened the doors to the forbidden subject of sex. He discovered, and publicly asserted, that the impulse for life is essentially sexual in nature, and it is the disturbance of this natural impulse in childhood and youth that lies at the root of human misery and neurosis.

Having made such a pioneering breakthrough, one would have thought that the next step for Freud would have been to lead human beings out of misery, into a happier, better world where physical pleasure and sexual fulfillment could claim their rightful place.

But, on the contrary, Freud declared this miserable state of affairs to be inevitable. In his view, human sexuality has to be curbed and repressed in order for civilized society to exist. Any society that permits free, uninhibited enjoyment of sex would, in his view, dissolve into chaos.

It is for this reason that I find Freud a perplexing character. I see him almost like a dedicated archaeologist searching the deserts of Northern Africa and Arabia for the legendary wealth of King Solomon's mines. Having at last found the mines, he then hurriedly closes the entrance again and declares it unsafe for anyone to enter and enjoy the fabulous treasure inside.

When I use the term 'fabulous treasure' in this context, I am not referring simply to the sex act, but to sex energy and its potential for fueling human growth in many dimensions, including the spiritual dimension.

155

As we shall see in the next section of this book, sex energy has infinite possibilities, but Freud stopped at the very first step and declared that the only option – and the sole function of his new science of psychoanalysis – is to help human beings adjust to a 'normal' state of sexual repression, for the sake of social order.

Reich rejected his teacher's thesis. While Freud saw sexual repression as necessary for civilization, Reich asserted that it is precisely this repression of sexual energy that prevents the creation of a truly civilized society in which people can be free from neurosis and naturally happy.

Searching for evidence to support his ideas, Reich was impressed by the report of a German anthropologist, Bronislaw Malinowski, who in the 1920's spent several years studying matriarchal tribal societies on the Trobriand Islands of the Pacific.

On the basis of this report, Reich wrote his own book, "The Invasion of Compulsory Sex Morality," comparing Trobriand and European cultures.

He noted that Trobriand children are free to explore their curiosity about sex, can examine each other's genitals and play sexually as much as they like. Parents and other adults find these early sexual adventures natural and don't interfere, extending to the children a general attitude of support and amused tolerance.

As teenagers, they develop more lasting relationships of a sexual nature, but these are not fixed or regulated by the parents. Each village has 'bachelor' houses where young couples can live together for as long as their love affairs last. These liaisons are not necessarily monogamous and there is an overall climate of individual freedom and experimentation. Sometimes, too, groups of teenagers venture to neighboring villages for parties involving sexual encounters.

For Reich, the vital issue is not that young people in Trobriand society can explore sexuality, which, he notes, also happens in Western societies, especially among the poorer classes. It is the attitude with which this exploration takes place that is the determining factor as far as individual happiness is concerned.

Among the Trobriand islanders, there is no sex-negating morality, no guilt, no sense of shame, no idea that sexual exploration is somehow dirty or forbidden. There are no crippling and debasing attitudes towards love life.

As a result, there is no armoring of the sexual organs and no damage to the natural flow of sex energy. This allows young people to enjoy full satisfaction in sexual embrace, whereas in Western societies, even when sexual intercourse occurs, the partners cannot achieve satisfaction because of chronic tension around their sexual organs.

According to Reich, based on his clinical investigations, almost all the women and over half the men in Western societies are sexually disturbed and incapable of any real sexual satisfaction, due to repression and genital armoring.

As for Freud's claim that a sexually permissive society must disintegrate, Reich noted that although Trobriand society is less industrially developed than Europe or America, it is stable, sophisticated and far more advanced as far as other cultural values are concerned.

For example, there is no neurosis, no misery, no voyeurism, no rape, no pornography. There is no fetishism, exhibitionism or even masturbation. There are no teenage suicides, no prostitution and no brothels.

Reich considered the enduring structure of Trobriand culture proof that society does not fall into disorder when sexual instincts are allowed and encouraged, and that moral control through the condemnation of sex is not necessary for civilization to happen.

Other investigators may have halted at this point, having satisfied their initial inquiries, but Reich, ever the scientific investigator, became even more curious. If sex negation is not necessary for civilized behavior, then why, he wondered, do modern societies so vigorously support the process of sexual denial and sexual repression?

He found clues in the same Trobriand culture, in a significant change in behavior that occurs after marriage. Suddenly, a different kind of morality enters, not so much concerned with sexual fidelity as public appearance. Severe social pressures are imposed on husband and wife – especially on the wife – to behave in accordance with a code of conduct that does not even allow the couple to show affection to each other in public.

The key to this change, Reich discovered, lies in the economic interests of the man, who receives a lifelong wedding gift from his wife's family of an annual supply of garden produce – the Trobriands being a farming society.

What Reich demonstrates is that the compulsion of marriage and morality is introduced to benefit male-dominated social structures, and heralds the beginning of a transition from matriarchal society to the patriarchal model that has dominated Western culture for several thousand years.

In other words, sexual morality serves economic interests. The woman must behave rightly, because she is traded as part of a complex business deal between two families that favors the rich and powerful members of society – usually, the chief's clan and other leading male members of the tribe.

Reich is not alone in his view. Anthropologists and historians generally agree that sexual morality and marital monogamy developed with the introduction of private property.

Reich also asserted that, as this new, authoritarian model of society evolved and became more dominant, sexual denial in childhood and youth was found to be necessary to make marriage work, because those who were free to enjoy sex – both men and women – were much less likely to remain faithful within the marriage structure.

In this way, sexual repression became the glue by which a certain type of society held itself together, serving the vested interests of a ruling clan, or class, who wanted to control the distribution of property and remain at the top of the social hierarchy.

Religion also benefited by condemning sexuality, because when people are miserable and neurotic they are easier to console with promises of future salvation. In this way, an unwritten contract came into existence between religious and political leaders, who developed a mutually beneficial system of controlling and manipulating people.

The net result, in terms of our customs today, is two genitally armored individuals entering into a lifelong contract of monogamous marriage without any hope of sexual fulfillment or personal happiness.

Reich's campaign to liberate people from sexual repression meant that he was opposed wherever he went, because he was attacking the foundations of exploitation. But he was not a political revolutionary, seeking to overthrow the ruling elite. He simply wanted people to be happy, free from neurosis, sexually healthy and naturally orgasmic.

First in Vienna, then Berlin, he opened sex clinics for working class people, giving advice on birth control, marriage problems and pregnancy, and writing pamphlets in favor of sexual freedom, especially for young people.

He was insistent on the right of children to be allowed to masturbate, from babyhood through puberty, and when puberty arrives, solid and clear instruction on birth control should be given so that teenagers can make love without fear.

Because of his campaign, Reich ended up almost alone. After his break with Freud he was virtually disowned by the entire psychoanalytic movement.

As a Marxist, he had friends in the European communist parties who at first supported his principles of sexual equality and freedom, but they, too, gradually deserted him and began to publicly criticize him.

This is a point worth understanding, because it reveals a basic conflict between politics and sex.

In 1933, Reich wrote a classic book, "The Mass Psychology of Fascism," showing how authoritarian regimes appeal to the public and manipulate the idealism of youth.

It was aimed against Hitler and the Nazi movement, but the communists with whom Reich aligned himself also wanted to manipulate the public, offering their own form of utopia that would be ushered in after the working classes seized power.

They feared that if Reich was successful in helping ordinary people take control over their own lives, enjoying sexual fulfillment and personal happiness, then public discontent would disappear and the motivation for violent revolution would be undermined.

It is to Reich's credit that he remained a scientist and humanitarian at heart, not a politician, and was willing to pay the price of being criticized, condemned and ostracized in order to stay focused on a single basic problem: how to get rid of human misery and neurosis, and help people enjoy life.

This is where I come into the picture, because, like Reich, I am in the business of helping people find happiness.

When ordinary people, for whatever reason, come to realize that they are living in an unfulfilling way, some of them start looking around for methods to free themselves from the confinement in which society has placed them.

That's when they come to me, or to people like me. That's when I introduce them to the de-armoring process, in which the sex center is the final segment.

Reich calls this the 'pelvic segment.' It includes the pelvis, genitals, anus, all the muscles around the hips, groin and buttocks, and the legs and feet. This corresponds to the first chakra in the chakra system, which governs the physical body, the lust for life, the basic drive to survive.

How does damage occur to this segment? Obviously, a general climate of sexual repression and taboo in a child's home environment is going to penetrate his or her psyche, even if nothing is said directly.

Unspoken messages can be delivered with a morning bowl of cornflakes. Conditioning can be by omission as well as prohibition. For example, if a child gets touched and caressed on all areas of the body except one, an idea will slowly form that this area is somehow forbidden, dirty or untouchable.

In my case, sex education was more direct. I discovered masturbation early. I must have been about three-and-half or

160

four years old when I went through a phase of masturbating openly, just touchy-touchy, yummy-yummy…nice, warm, fuzzy feelings in my genital area.

At a certain point, my mother said, "Don't do that, and certainly don't do it when other people are around."

I received a whole training about keeping my hands above the covers of my bed at night, plus a reward system of chocolate cookies for doing so, as well as little scoldings for disobeying.

It was an elaborate effort to steer me away from masturbation, but somehow I knew the whole time that what I was doing was okay. I never bought that it was bad. I just had to keep it secret. As long my parents couldn't figure out that I was doing it, it was okay. So masturbation remained a kind of secret companion through my childhood and teenage years.

In addition to the armoring effect of this kind of sex education – perhaps anti-sex education is a more accurate term – there is also the impact of sexual abuse. This is a huge area, ranging from the leering looks of an ageing relative to sexual penetration and intercourse with children by adults or older siblings.

It is only recently that this very private and personal issue has become a subject of public debate, resulting in a growing understanding that almost everyone has been abused in one way or another – if not physically, or violently, then at least through some invasive way of looking or talking.

Pedophiles are experts in understanding children and how to manipulate them, often by becoming friends with their parents and thereby isolating the child from its main source of protection and safety.

In one case that was related to me during a session, a woman explained how a neighbor had compelled her to make love with him, when she was about nine years old, by threatening to tell her parents that she had kissed young boys while playing in the neighborhood.

To prevent him from 'telling on her,' the man extracted a promise that she would do something for him, and only

afterwards did she discover what this 'something' entailed –
three acts of sexual intercourse.

The whole idea was repugnant, but the man's threat that he
would tell her parents about the kissing incidents was enough to
force her into submission. It sounds totally implausible but it
worked.

Most of us can recall a psychological atmosphere in
childhood or puberty of sexual innuendo and sly remarks, which
also contributes to sexual armoring – for example, a horny old
grandfather who lives in the upstairs room for most of your
childhood and every once in a while pinches you.

I had an uncle like that, a young, rakish kind of guy who was
always muttering things out of the side of his mouth, like "Heh,
heh, heh...." Once in a while, he'd grab me, pinch me or tickle
me, saying, "Aren't you cute!"

I hated it and wanted to smack him and say, "Get away from
me, you creep!" But, of course, I never did, because, as a child,
it never occurred to me that I had the right or the authority to do
such a thing to an adult relative. He never did anything serious,
but these people don't have to do much to create a certain vibe
that affects a growing child's sexual energy.

As you can see from these examples, there are all kinds of
manipulations around sexuality. It is the most abused of our
natural capacities because we need it, we want it, we are
flooded with its energy, driven to seek gratification, and yet at
the same time there are tremendous taboos and regulations
surrounding it.

The conventional, repressive solution to this problem is
rather like filling a pot with water, nailing down the lid, putting
it on the stove and turning up the gas – sooner or later,
something is going to explode.

In Pulsation, we take a totally different approach: dissolving
armoring and releasing tension in and around the pelvic area, so
that sexual energy can be re-awakened, lived and celebrated.

From the beginning of any Pulsation group, we are
constantly working with the pelvic segment because this is

where our vitality originates. Once it is released, sex energy can flow all over the body.

In a way, it is like crude oil. As it ascends through the other segments and the chakras it becomes more refined, expressing itself in a non-genital, non-sexual way. But the basic fuel and power for all these expressions is sex. Even the immensely pleasurable belly sensations I described in the previous chapter, or the overflowing love of an open heart, have their source in sex energy.

This is the Tantric understanding that we will be exploring in the next section, and it is also my personal experience – both as a therapist and in my private life.

For this reason, even though we go into the de-armoring process working from the top down, we keep charging the body with sex energy, using the breathing and body movements I described earlier.

At the same time, whenever we build up energy and discharge emotion, we are following the formula of sexual orgasm. The same quality of convulsive release is experienced with our emotions, and this is the basic tool of the de-armoring process.

However, even though we are working with sex energy from the beginning, I know that I cannot approach the sex center directly until armoring has been loosened in the other six segments.

It's no accident that the pelvic segment is the last in the series. Sex lies in the deepest depths of our biology, and sexual and pleasure issues lie at the deepest root of our psychology, so approaching the armoring of this segment is a delicate task.

One thing I want to make clear is that I never touch the genital area while working, precisely because it is so private and delicate. This area has often been so traumatized that direct contact would only re-traumatize and deepen any wounds.

In addition, direct contact with the genitals may provoke sexual arousal, which is not the point in the de-armoring process. The aim is to release tension and restore energy flow, not to stimulate the sexual zone.

163

There are plenty of other ways to approach this segment, using deep breathing into the sex center, pelvic movements, leg kicking, massaging tense muscles.

At times, I may press deeply into the thigh adductors, the muscles of the inner thigh, which Reich calls 'the morality muscles,' because these are the ones that are used – especially by women – to keep the legs closed and prevent access to the sexual organs.

I may also encourage the client to tighten and release muscles in the pelvic floor, between the anus and genitals, as this helps to loosen pelvic armoring.

With experience, it is easy to see when someone has been sexually abused, just by observing breathing and body movements while the work is happening.

For example, during a simple exercise like breathing into the pelvis, while at the same lifting the pelvis and rocking it back – a movement similar to love-making – clients with issues of abuse usually start to get uncomfortable.

They show expressions of anxiety, shifting and moving in a way that reduces the effectiveness of the exercise, trying to divert attention from the pelvic area.

Also, the eyes tend to glass over – this can happen even before the work has started. I remember interviewing one woman, who had applied to join a Tantric Pulsation workshop, and asking her, "Do you have a history of sexual abuse?"

The woman, who came from Russia, suddenly turned into a robot. She looked away from me, her eyes got glassy – she almost went into a kind of trance. I was talking to her, but she wouldn't look at me and began to reply in a tiny, sing-song voice.

It was clear that she didn't want to face this issue, and that to begin to reclaim her sexual energy she would need to address a whole package of issues: denial of pain, rejection of men, anger at parents....

For this, a sexual deconditioning group is needed, or individual sessions, to explore and heal these issues.

In Pulsation, when people have done a fair amount of de-armoring work, they naturally start to connect to the pelvis and may start to feel pleasurable sensations. But they may also feel shy, embarrassed or guilty. It's important for the therapist to see both aspects – the pleasure and the guilt – because this is one of the splits we discover in the pelvis.

We see a capacity for pleasure and the longing of the body to enjoy it, but at the same time there is a veneer of conditioning overlaying it, filled with all kinds of dos and don'ts, shoulds and should nots.

I encourage people to acknowledge old feelings of guilt but also to jump over them, giving themselves permission to stay with the pleasure. This is usually not difficult, because by this time, when the upper segments have been loosened, there is a certain amount of emotional space available. People have a certain distance from which they can see how guilt and shame stand in the way of their pleasure.

If I can encourage a person to move the pelvis a bit more, to breathe into the sex center a bit more, to allow a gentle pulsation of the pelvis and even make pleasurable sounds, this can help them stay connected with the pelvis – not just the genitals but the whole pelvic area – as a source of pleasure and vitality.

Talking is important at this stage, because when I see a client is passing through a layer of guilt and shame, I'll gently inquire, "Who made you feel ashamed? Who made you feel embarrassed about your sex?"

The client may say, "My mother."

I'll ask the person to stay in contact with the pleasurable feelings and to talk to his, or her, mother, saying things like, "See mom, I'm a sexual person and it's okay. There's nothing wrong in it. I feel good like this. I have a right to be sexual. I have a right to enjoy my sexuality."

Affirmative statements like these can be very supportive in opening the whole pelvic area energetically.

Usually, by this time, when we have worked down through the segments, into the depths of the body, clients are very

165

willing to explore and express whatever they discover. They find it's good to go into these dark, forbidden places, into the anger, guilt and frustration of not being allowed to live their sexuality, because they know it is a freeing and liberating experience.

Once these things have been brought to light and released, the next step can only be pleasure, because that's at the base, that's at the root, that is at the core of our natural striving as a biological organism – the movement towards pleasure.

When armor has been loosened in the pelvis, this is the point at which we can integrate all the segments, experiencing a unity of energy as it flows freely up and down the length of the body. In this we find deep pleasure, contentment, a sense of oneness with existence.

I use an exercise called Soft Pulsation as a way for people to experience this unity, this sense of wholeness in the body. The exercise is usually done alone, as an inner and private experience.

Participants adopt the basic breathing position, lying on their backs on a mat, knees raised and bent, breathing into the hollow energy tube that extends all the way down into the belly and sex.

I guide people to tune into their breathing, feeling an ocean-like flow of breath filling and emptying the body. Gradually, I invite them to allow a soft rocking movement of the pelvis, in rhythm with the breathing, retracting it on the inhale, arching the back slightly, then swinging the pelvis forward on the exhale.

It is important to synchronize this movement with breath, because it will help to create a deepening wave of energy that pulsates in the body, washing up and down, filling each segment, energizing and charging every cell.

Because blocks in the segments have loosened, there is a good possibility to experience an uninhibited and continuous wave of energy flowing up and down the body, as well as from core to periphery.

This wave, when allowed and embraced, brings sensations of pleasure, aliveness, and an oceanic joy, similar to that felt by lovers after a total orgasmic experience. It proves that this is available to each of us as individuals, in our aloneness as well as with a beloved.

As the breathing and pelvic movements continue, as the energy wave deepens, I suggest introducing other harmonious movements into the exercise, using arms, hands, mouth, head, gradually including the whole body.

The exercise may last 20-30 minutes, or even 45 minutes if people are able to allow themselves that much pleasure.

In my experience, though, most people have levels of tolerance for high-charge pleasurable sensations in the body, a kind of built-in time limit, after which negative feelings resurface as a way of discharging excess energy which is becoming uncomfortable.

When a body is in balance, it can accumulate and hold a charge of energy without having to discharge it, instead, enjoying the light, pleasurable tension of a contained charge.

Most of the 'rough stuff,' like banging the pelvis on the mat, screaming and shouting in anger, hate or disgust, have hopefully been released so it is easier to keep the energy charge in the body at a higher level and enjoy its qualities.

In this balanced state, we can open to the subtler realms of rising energy, intimacy, meditation, presence… in short, to the world of Tantra.

PART THREE

The Map of Pleasure

Preface to Part Three

In presenting my work to the public, I offer two kinds of workshops: Pulsation, focusing on de-armoring the body, freeing energy flow and encouraging emotional expression; and Tantric Pulsation, helping people experience the upward movement of energy through the body, from its sexual origins towards meditation.

Because of this division, some people may think these are two different processes, but really they are part of one organic Tantric approach.

My discovery and creation of Tantric Pulsation has grown out of the neo-Reichian work I originally trained in and practiced for many years. The Eastern influence of meditation and spiritual practice that developed out of my years in India brought a deep awareness of more subtle energies – states of consciousness, silence, grace – adding the Tantric dimension.

As will become clear in this section of my book, Tantra spans the whole range of human experience, beginning with the raw animal energy of the body and moving upwards toward an experience of the divine.

So, even though this section focuses on what is offered in my Tantric Pulsation groups, I would not like the reader to assume that the Pulsation work described in the first two sections is not Tantric by nature.

It is one organic approach to the human condition. It is a journey of human energy from its animal origins to its spiritual flowering.

Tantric Pulsation offers ordinary people the opportunity to learn and practice different energy techniques that they can integrate into their daily lives, enriching their ongoing relationships.

171

The Tantric Pulsation process is most effective with people who have done some body-oriented personal growth work to loosen their muscular armoring, so their energy can flow freely without constraints of psychological and emotional blocks.

However, it can also be done, under skilled guidance, by relative beginners who are open to a new kind of self-exploration.

Chapter Thirteen

The Tantra Experience

I did not study Tantra. I lived it. One fine day, I walked in through the gate of a spiritual community in India where the very air was pulsating with the energy of Tantra, and from that moment on I have been exploring the Tantric experience.

In fact, although I did not know it, I had been walking the path of Tantra even before I arrived in India, because ever since I can remember I felt a basic 'yes' towards life, and this 'yes' is the essence of the Tantric approach.

It is the path of acceptance, non-denial, embracing all that life has to offer, from the mundane to the sacred, from sex to Samadhi.

The history of Tantra as a spiritual movement in India – where it flourished, what rituals were performed, why it was suppressed and became a secret, underground movement – has never been my primary focus.

In his discourses, Osho explained the Tantra vision, its implications, and its importance as a spiritual path, but neither was he much interested in historic details. His whole effort was to make Tantra a contemporary, living force that we could experience immediately and directly, in our own bodies. And in this he was dramatically successful.

I say 'dramatically,' because his small ashram became, for a while, an intense pressure cooker of exploration in which hundreds, then thousands, of people participated. It was an intense, explosive, revolutionary, highly controversial experiment that caught the media's attention, worried India's politicians, and attracted courageous seekers and adventurers from all over the world.

173

Perhaps the best way to introduce it is to tell my own story, because when I arrived in 1976 the experiment was still in its infancy, just beginning to take off. My personal experiences will also help to illustrate the context in which my Tantric Pulsation work developed.

I came to India via Europe, where, as I mentioned in chapter three, I had begun to lead Reichian workshops. It was in London that I got to know my first *sannyasins* – as Osho's disciples were called – and it was they who had introduced me to Dynamic Meditation. From there, I flew to Bombay, or Mumbai as it is now called.

Osho's ashram was located in Pune, about 120 miles east of Mumbai. At first glance, the place didn't look like much, just two or three large, colonial-style houses in a sleepy suburb of the city, with a small meditation hall tucked around the back.

But it didn't take me long to be seduced by a mysterious quality that hung in the air, especially at night when it was a little bit smoky, filled with scents from night flowers and strange cries from exotic birds, plus a chorus of crickets and frogs in abundance.

There was an intense vibe, or energy, inside the ashram that I could hardly separate from the warm sub-tropical climate. It all seemed to blend together when I walked in the gate – an atmosphere I was able to absorb that soon overrode any feeling about how ordinary the place looked.

There were about a hundred Westerners among the Indian sannyasins, most of them working in ashram jobs and positions, and I liked what was happening between them. There was a lot of laughing, a feeling of genuine, heartfelt warmth, and I especially noticed their long, intimate, hugs that seemed to go on for hours.

I could walk past a man and woman, hugging on a path, on my way to the canteen for a cup of chai – the delicious Indian blend of thick, milky, spicy, sweet tea – and when I walked back half an hour later they'd still be standing there, wrapped around each other, totally self-absorbed.

It wasn't necessarily sexual, even though full body contact was happening. It was an energy phenomenon – I could sometimes feel the heat as I passed them – and I must say I found it intriguing and attractive.

I saw Osho for the first time while attending his morning discourse, but I can't say that his presence had an immediate impact on me. There was a certain excitement and curiosity – 'My god, I'm here in India and this man is said to be an enlightened master' – but the experience of being able to absorb his energy in any deep kind of way took a while to develop.

In Europe, I'd seen photos of Osho, so physically he was more or less the way I expected: bald with a gray beard, big brown eyes that sparkled when he smiled, not very tall, wearing a simple white robe.

On my second day at the ashram, I asked to be initiated as a sannyasin. I'd already made the decision in Europe, because it was obvious that whatever I was hoping to experience with Osho could only happen through participation. And besides, I've always been the kind of girl who jumps first and asks questions later.

There were about 15 people in my first 'darshan,' as the evening meeting with Osho was called, and it was held in the same small auditorium where he gave discourse.

When it was my turn, I sat in front of him and he asked me to close my eyes while he wrote my new name on a piece of paper. Then he touched my third eye with his thumb.

Slowly, behind closed lids, my eyes rolled upward to the place where he was touching and, after a few moments, he said, "Good," and took his hand away. It seemed as though he was waiting for me to turn in, inside myself, before leaving my third eye.

Then he asked me to open my eyes and showed me my name: Deva Aneesha, explaining that 'deva' means 'divine' and 'aneesha' means 'godlessness.'

What a paradox – to be both divine and godless!

Osho went on to explain that, for him, paradox is the very spirit and law of life.

"God is not a person," he said. "In fact there is no God – there is only divine energy. It is better to call it godliness rather than God. Life is divine, but there is no god like a father-figure, there is

175

nobody who is manipulating, controlling – nobody has ever created life, it is eternal."

He said that religions with a father figure are childish and that the great religions of the East, like the one founded by Gautam Buddha, are for grown-up people who do not need a god.

He also said that he had been waiting for me, and I thought this remark may have had something to do with the fact that I was a group leader from Esalen. I'd already sent him a copy of my 'Pulsation and Feeling' booklet, which remains to this day in his personal library, and I'd written a dedication in it, placing myself and my skills at his service.

I knew that a diverse program of Western therapies and eastern meditations was being offered at the ashram, and it seemed natural to me that if I was going to be there for any length of time, I would also work there.

I had to wait a while for that to happen, because I was scheduled to lead more workshops in Europe and the US, but on that first visit I did have time to plunge into the group process myself, which was totally unlike anything I'd encountered at Esalen.

These groups were wild, intense, no-limit structures in which all of the repressed emotional and sexual energy that people had been sitting on for their whole lives was encouraged to be expressed.

Combined with Dynamic Meditation, held every morning at six o'clock, plus other meditation techniques designed to awaken and move energy, it proved a potent cocktail that blew away our collective veneer of social morality and polite behavior.

In these groups, I fought, kicked, screamed, wept, made love and was generally forced by the extremity of many situations to make an inner quantum leap that left the person I thought I was far behind. In doing so, I discovered energy resources and raw animal emotions I never imagined I possessed.

Later on, I came to realize that, in a very real sense, these groups didn't end. Or you can say that life in Pune was one long group. The ever-changing flux of love affairs, sexual encounters and relationships among the growing international community of sannyasins ensured that experiencing intense feelings continued, almost day and night.

I remember one particular occasion, while doing a Vipassana meditation retreat inside the ashram, when I was confronted with extreme jealousy.

Vipassana is not supposed to be a confrontational group. It is a classic Buddhist meditation, in which you sit silently, with closed eyes, watching your own breath moving in and out, and the rise and fall of your belly with the breathing. You are faced with your aloneness – and that's it.

But it so happened that my boyfriend of those times had a distinctive pair of shoes, which, whenever we went out of the meditation room for our 'Zen walk,' I noticed were lying outside the room next door, where a very attractive young woman was living.

I saw those shoes every day for ten days and all I could do about it was sit silently, breathe deeply, and watch my mind go crazy.

The navigator who guided us through this maze of intensity was Osho himself, who talked to us every morning for ninety minutes. His discourses were based on sayings and sutras from enlightened beings of the past – Gautam Buddha, Lao Tzu, Patanjali, Kabir, Jesus, a whole range of Zen, Sufi and Tantra masters – but his basic message was to nourish an inner flame of awareness, or consciousness, with which to see and understand everything we were experiencing.

According to Osho, spiritual growth requires our total energy and this can be accessed only when our repressed emotions, blocked sexuality, unconscious psychological patterns – jealousy, comparison, inferiority, guilt – have been brought into the light of awareness and dissolved.

It is the transformation of these energies, no matter how poisonous or destructive, that brings unity to a human being and opens the door to higher states of consciousness.

"What I am saying is absolutely alive, new, fresh, young," Osho explained. "It is not traditional at all. Hence I call my Tantra, Neo-Tantra. It is a totally different phenomenon.

"All ancient religions, Tantra or other, are ritualistic. Now man has become a grown-up, man has come of age. Those days of childhood are no more there. Those rituals look stupid.

"We have to free Tantra from all ritualistic patterns. We have to make it more poetic, more spontaneous, less patterned, less structured. That's what I am doing."

To my surprise and delight, Osho also talked about Wilhelm Reich. He said that although Reich had no idea about Tantra, he was developing methods of healing people's sexual problems that were similar to Tantric techniques created thousands of years earlier.

He agreed with Reich's theory of body armoring – how the body carries past memories stored in the muscles as chronic tension. He also said that Reich's understanding of how energy expands when a person feels loving, and shrinks when he is not, is really a description of the human aura – also known for centuries in the East.

"He was one of the greatest revolutionaries ever, and he has remained unknown, unrespected, unremembered," Osho commented, adding that there is still great potential in Reich's work if it can be developed in collaboration with Tantra.

When I began to lead my own group, in August 1977, Osho gave it the name 'Anatta,' a Buddhist term meaning 'no self.' So, a woman called 'godlessness' was leading a group called 'no self.'

No god and no self...it didn't leave much for me to cling to, which perhaps was the intention behind it, and a few weeks later I had a powerful insight into why Osho used such terms.

At the end of each group, participants and leaders were invited to come to evening darshan, where they could ask questions to Osho about whatever had happened during the process – or, indeed, about anything that was concerning them. Group leaders sat in the front row, so that evening I was sitting very close to Osho, almost directly in front of him.

I had been sitting there for the entire darshan, enjoying myself in a quiet and peaceful way. I remember feeling that every word he was saying just fell inside me and rested there. It wasn't what he said, but the 'vibe' of his saying it. For the first time, I was allowing myself to absorb and drink his presence.

The darshan ended and Osho started to get up from his chair to leave, bringing his hands together in the familiar Indian namaste with which he always greeted us. Just before he stood up, he made eye contact with me and then held my gaze, looking at me all the way from a sitting to standing position. It couldn't have taken more than a few seconds, but it seemed like forever. Then he proceeded to namaste the whole crowd and left the auditorium.

This look...

What was transmitted through this look, through the eye contact we had, I couldn't say. But it penetrated deep, deep inside me, and I felt I'd received such a vast amount of 'something' that I could barely contain it.

My head fell down to the floor and I started to cry. I was crying out of gratitude, out of the humbling experience of receiving such an incredible gift. But I couldn't even name it. In fact, it wasn't what he gave that touched me so deeply. It was his giving, his sharing – to me, to each one of us – in such an open-handed way, an unconditional and unreserved pouring of 'something' that I must have been ready to receive in that moment.

It was unexplainable. It was wordless. It was a transmission of divine energy, like the leaping of a flame from one candle to another. It was a receiving of 'something' that can also be called 'nothing.'

Then I understood the value of doing away with concepts like self and God, because whatever transpires in that mysterious dimension called 'spirituality' is so beyond all words, ideas and concepts that they can only hinder the transmission. It truly passes all understanding.

In the early days of leading the Anatta group, my work didn't change in any radical way. There were a number of exercises and structures I'd learned from Chuck and Erica Kelley, used in the Radix work, and these formed the backbone of the five-day workshop I was leading.

I was not in a hurry to change my style and nobody was pushing me to do so. I knew that some therapists were receiving detailed guidance from Osho about what they should do in their groups, but there was never anything like that with me.

Once in a while, in darshan, a participant would sit in front of Osho and describe something that was going on with him – perhaps energetically, in the body, or perhaps psychologically.

When this happened, Osho would sometimes turn to me and ask, "What do you think, Aneesha?"

I would say something which, to me, seemed rather superficial and obvious, such as pointing out a constriction in the person's diaphragm and a related incapacity to breathe deeply – nothing very profound in terms of spirituality or meditation. But Osho would nod and say, "That's exactly right," and then go back to talking with the person.

So I felt supported by him in a general way. He really gave me a lot of space to get on with the work in whatever way I saw fit.

Looking back, I can see the changes that happened in my work evolved not from any ideas, theories or guidance, but from my own personal experiences in Osho's energy field, so I will spend a little time talking about them.

Above all, those years in Pune were a journey into my aloneness, my private, inner world. And this was one of those paradoxes Osho talked about, because on the surface I was living a very social life. I was right in the middle of an expanding community of hundreds of sannyasins, I was deeply involved with them, I had lovers and friends, I was totally participating in the commune, leading groups and sessions.

But there was another, very different part of me that was running side by side with the outer life. This was the seeker, the meditator in me, who went every day to sit for an hour and a half, silently listening to Osho's morning discourse, using his words and the spaces between them to sink deeper and deeper into herself. This was the one who, before or after work, participated regularly in the ashram's daily program of meditation techniques.

My love affair with different techniques went on for months and years. Sometimes I would get on a run with Dynamic, held early each morning. Sometimes it was Kundalini Meditation, held each evening at sunset. Sometimes it was Vipassana, sometimes Sufi Dance – a lively celebration of singing and dancing.

The Pune ashram, as I kept discovering, wasn't a normal kind of ashram. Meditation was the backbone of what was happening, but celebration came a close second. In Osho's vision of life, meditation without celebration is too dry, while celebration without meditation lacks depth. A synthesis is needed, so the ashram's daily program offered many opportunities for singing and dancing, both of which I loved.

When I was a teenager I used to dance – rock 'n roll, this kind of stuff – and I also played guitar and sang folk songs, or tunes from musicals. But when I became an adult, moved to California and became a working therapist, these things disappeared from my life. Somehow, there wasn't the space for it.

In Pune, it all came back with a rush. Every night, there was singing and dancing in Buddha Hall – a newly-built, much bigger meditation space that could accommodate the growing number of visitors.

Hearing Osho speak of the importance of celebration and then experiencing it in my own body – the value of singing and how blissful it made me feel – was a revelation. To sing my heart out, to dance madly, to really experience the moment when a dancer disappears and only the dance remains…these were some of my most precious experiences.

If someone were to ask me what I got out of those early years in Pune I'd have to say that the lifestyle, as a whole, was far more important than any single experience or point of understanding. Osho called this collective phenomenon a 'buddhafield,' where a group of seekers enhance each other's growth process simply by being together with an enlightened master in the same energy field.

The understanding that I developed for my work, which I now share with others, came to me organically, through just living that life, experiencing my own energy through the daily meditations, the celebrations, the work.

The nature of my work in Anatta started to change when Osho began giving 'energy darshans' at the end of 1978.

Ever since I'd first arrived in Pune, I noticed that Osho often worked with the energy of individuals in darshan. Sometimes he'd use a flashlight, which seemed to help him perceive the aura surrounding a person's body, sometimes he'd ask people to close their eyes and allow movement or sounds while he touched the third eye or heart.

On these occasions, he asked female sannyasins to come and sit behind the person on whom he was working, thereby acting as a medium for his energy – helping the energy to flow through the person sitting in front of him. A few times he called me up for this task, which I thoroughly enjoyed.

Then Osho introduced a new dimension in the evening darshans. In addition to giving sannyas initiation, answering questions, saying farewell or welcoming people back, he now gave 'energy darshan' in which there was no talking.

People would come, two at a time, and sit in front of Osho, then be surrounded by female mediums – maybe a dozen in all – arranged in certain patterns, all somehow linked to each other.

Osho would ask everyone in the auditorium to raise their arms, close their eyes and start humming and swaying. Wild music would fill the air, the lights would flash on and off, people would be humming and sometimes screaming ecstatically, and we would all dive into this ocean of 'nothing' that would rise up and engulf us.

I was not one of the regular mediums, called every night, but as a group leader I was coming to darshan quite often and loved this new energy process, enjoying every second of it. I would raise my arms, start humming, let my body sway and almost immediately I would have a strong experience of energy rising through my body, all the way from my sex center through my heart to the top of my head.

It altered forever my understanding about energy. It gave me first-hand experience of the Tantric principles that Osho had talked about in discourse, moving from the animal through the human to the divine.

It also took me beyond Reich, because he stopped at the human, while I was experiencing an upward movement that took me beyond the limitations of the physical form, melting and merging with a vast sea of divine energy.

Osho seemed to be the immediate source of this energy, but, as he himself explained, he was only a doorway through which we could access something much, much bigger than any individual. He had already disappeared into this ocean and could therefore make it available to others.

Every time I went to energy darshan I experienced the phenomenon of rising energy and, of course, when I sat directly in front of him, in the middle of the mediums, it was particularly strong. His personal touch on my third eye was a provocation for my energy to rush upwards in an orgasmic expansion of cosmic dimensions that was clearly beyond the mind – what Zen people call 'No Mind.'

In fact, the experience was so powerful for so many people that a team of young men, called 'lifters,' would be ready at the end of each session to gently carry away those who had been so overwhelmed by the experience that they were temporarily unable to walk.

Even when I was not in darshan, I would participate outside, because the whole ashram was plunged into darkness when the energy sessions began, so if I was sitting in my room, or singing in the evening music group, I'd just stop whatever I was doing and feel the energy. It was a very important part of my day.

Based on what was happening to me in energy darshan, I began to understand that the chakra system and Reich's segments are really part of the same phenomenon, functioning at different levels. The muscle segments are on the periphery – physical and obvious – while the chakras add an energetic dimension that penetrates deeper and deeper to the core of the body.

In my groups, I introduced ways to help people connect energetically with the chakras, infusing them with vitality in much the same way that I was doing with the muscle segments.

About a year later, I felt the need to develop a different kind of group. I'd always worked in a structured way and now felt that it would be interesting and challenging for me to function without structure.

I asked Osho if I could lead a three-day workshop in which I could experiment with non-structure, and he gave me a group called Sahaj, which in the ancient Indian Sanskrit language means 'spontaneity.'

While leading Sahaj, I was interested to see in which directions the energy tumbled each day. Sometimes I would help it along, sometimes I just let the participants get on with it by themselves. Sometimes, the whole group would simply curl up in a big ball, relax and do nothing. Then the energy would somehow shift and change and the group would start exploding, with people running around, playing like kids, screaming and yelling. Then it would change again, calm down perhaps, becoming more soft and sensual.

It was through leading this group that I learned to trust the spontaneous flow of energy through a group of people, rather like the dynamics you see in a school of fish or a flock of birds, as they all suddenly change direction.

I also asked if I could lead a group called Pulsation – the first group I led with that name – to experiment with what I was learning in the energy darshans.

In it, I developed structures where people would sway like seaweed on the ocean floor, as if gently pushed and pulled by invisible currents of energy. I also played with energy mandalas, linking people to each other while sitting in circles and other patterns.

I used belly dance and rhythmic, snake-like movements to awaken energy in the pelvic segment and help it rise through the body. I worked very consciously to help people discover a new dimension of sensitivity, especially in touch – more feminine, receptive, non-doing.

In 1981, when Osho and his sannyasins went to America and started building a new commune on a big ranch in Central Oregon, I went to Europe for a while and led groups in several countries. Then I shifted to the ranch and divided my time between constructing houses – which I loved – and leading groups for visitors.

Our stay in the USA lasted four and a half years. This is not the place to describe that saga: the amazing speed with which we built a whole city, and the battle that developed between our community and just about the whole of America.

Suffice it to say that Osho's radical vision of life, and our enthusiastic ability to turn it into reality, invited more or less the same reaction as that given to Wilhelm Reich. And, like Reich, Osho would not compromise to save himself.

After being arrested, jailed and deported in November 1985, Osho traveled the world looking for a new place to stay, but in the end returned to Pune, where I joined him in 1987 and began leading groups again as a new community started growing around him.

It was at this time that I began to offer trainings, giving people hands-on experience of how to work with Reichian techniques and conduct individual sessions. This was when I started calling the Reichian work 'Pulsation.'

Osho died in January 1990, but the community in Pune continued and I never forgot his comment that Reich and Tantra could be developed together. For me, this became the seed of a new process, Tantric Pulsation, which I now offer as a kind of sub-branch to my Pulsation work.

This section of my book is devoted to explaining how Tantric Pulsation functions.

Chapter Fourteen

The Tantric Milieu

A certain atmosphere is needed as part of our entry into the world of Tantra, and here I am not talking about the need to create a special physical environment. I am referring more to a psychological milieu.

Tantra requires an atmosphere that invites people to relax, to trust, to understand that they are in a safe place where sensitive processes like opening, sharing, and remaining vulnerable can happen in a way that will be respectfully received.

In the de-armoring section of this book, I have talked in detail about the Feeling Pairs as a map for understanding movements of energy experienced as feelings and emotions. The focus was on provoking and expressing the negative aspect of the pairs: anger, fear and pain.

In my Tantric work, the exploration focuses more deeply on the positive qualities of the Feeling Pairs: love, trust and pleasure. These softer, more delicate feelings require a safe, protected space in order to emerge.

Ordinarily, our day-to-day lives don't offer such spaces. To be sure, there are relaxing moments, there are warm and heartful moments, but at the same time there are plenty of hard knocks and unpleasant surprises.

For example, you are with the man you love, and you feel it's time to open up and be honest about your insecurity. Up to now, you have felt that part of your personality – the weak, vulnerable, self-doubting part – had to be hidden in order to fulfill your role as the ideal female companion, but now the strain is getting too much and you want to let him know the shadow side is there.

Then suddenly... slam! He reacts by closing down emotionally, denying the problem, blaming you, walking out, or by any of the well-known methods that make you remember why you chose to be self-protective and secretive in the first place.

Such incidents are all too common and they are experienced by men as well as women. For example, taking the man's view, perhaps you have been hiding the fact that you find yourself frequently thinking about, or looking at, other women. Now you feel it's time to share this irritating mental undercurrent. It's not that you actually want to be unfaithful to your longtime lover; it's just that you're tired of hiding things.

But instead of appreciating your honesty, your desire for intimate sharing, your female partner explodes in a fit of jealousy, threatens to end the relationship and bursts into tears.

This is why we tend to live an armored life, because we've experienced so many times that when we start to open up, start to reveal our vulnerability, many negative things can happen. We can be disrespected, we can be rejected, punished, manipulated.

In Tantric Pulsation, it's important to create a protective and supportive atmosphere, and in this chapter I want to talk about how I do that – the things I say and do, the ways I suggest people behave with each other, that help them to open and move deeper into these energy experiments.

In the days prior to the group I interview the prospective participants, to make sure they are ready for this Tantric exploration. One question I ask is whether they have a history of abuse in childhood – particularly sexual abuse – that up to now has not been addressed in therapy.

This is an important question, because in the Tantra dimension of my work I don't focus on dealing with traumatic issues. Rather, the Tantric orientation is on enjoying and exploring sexual energy, adopting an adventurous attitude. For this reason, I refer people with abuse to other therapeutic processes before recommending Tantra.

I also try to balance the number of men and women – important for the partner exercises that follow. I accept people of all ages, from early twenties to late sixties, but the vast majority of participants are in their thirties and early forties.

These 'thirty-something' people are very interested, I find, in meditative Tantric practices. Why? Because they've had the experience of regular sex, they've tried everything, they've 'been there, done that,' and their sexual energy is still active and moving so they're looking for something different.

Now they want to find out what can happen when sexuality acquires an inward focus, and this is what Tantra implies: meditating in intimacy with another, practicing meditation techniques with a lover or partner.

The first day of the workshop begins with dance. It's always good to move the body, waking up our physical energy before sitting down and talking, or introducing exercises.

Even though the beginning is similar to a regular Pulsation workshop, there is a qualitative difference about Tantra. These people have come together specifically in order to meet each other in a way that engages their sexual energy, and this adds a certain spice and nervousness to the proceedings

Just the word 'Tantra' triggers all kinds of ideas about sex. And, attracted as people are to explore their sexual energy, they're also afraid. There are many layers of conditioning, absorbed from the surrounding culture and social environment – from parents, teachers, priests, the media, peer groups – so people often feel ashamed about the whole subject.

Simply looking into each other's eyes may trigger a feeling of shyness, or fear of rejection, so as the music starts to play and people start to dance, I pick up the microphone and seduce them into an attitude of playful exploration.

"This workshop is an opportunity to enjoy yourselves, to enjoy each other, in a light and easy way," I explain. "So move your energy now...dancing, moving around the room, seeing who is here. You can flirt with your eyes, play with your eyes...and keep moving, keep breathing...."

"There's no need to get married to anyone. This is an invitation to meet without consequences."

189

I spend a good deal of time encouraging them to let their playfulness come out and at the same time assuring them that nothing really serious is going to happen. Sexual issues in our culture have become shrouded with very serious, weighty implications, with consequences like pregnancy, marriage, children, setting up a home.

Here, we are meeting to enjoy sexual energy with simplicity, natural fun and above all friendliness. I want men and women to enter this journey together as friends and fellow travelers, taking down the walls created by centuries of prejudice.

"Just keep meeting, keep changing," I say. "You're going to have many partners over the next five days, so don't start thinking, 'God, I better find somebody quick, because what if I get stuck with the wrong one!' Don't worry. You're not going to get pinned to one person."

One of the most helpful tools for creating the right atmosphere for this kind of group, from start to finish, is music. There are many different kinds of music, invoking many different spaces and qualities. I use music to raise the energy, to create a charge, to get people dancing hard and fast. I use it to soften, to relax, to touch feelings and emotions. I play heartful music that can bring up tears and deeply quiet music that invites a silent turning inwards.

At the beginning, I play lively, juicy, sexy dance songs, with lyrics like, for example, "That's the way, uh-huh, uh-huh, I like it..." – music that invites people to flirt, spark off each other, have fun and let their bodies have little conversations on the dance floor that lighten the atmosphere while at the same time charging and energizing the participants.

After three or four dances, the music goes off and I ask them to stop and close their eyes, bringing the focus of attention inside.

"Stand silently for a moment, feeling your feet on the floor, your legs supporting you," I guide them. "You can bend your knees a little bit, that will help you feel your connection with the earth."

It's time to take the energy a little deeper, making these male-female connections more intimate. In this way, my approach is a step-by-step progression. Introducing people to the Tantric world, I need to show one piece of the territory, one section of the map, at a time, creating an understanding that allows us to move to the next step.

I invite people to open their eyes and walk around the room, making eye contact with the other participants. As they do so, I verbalize what's probably going on inside their minds, saying things like, "You may be feeling shy as you walk around, that's okay. It's natural in a roomful of strangers to feel a bit shy. Keep walking, keep looking, keep breathing and feeling this shyness, letting it be there."

"Notice, to whom you feel attracted, with whom you may have something already bubbling, where there is energy...."

After a while, I ask them to choose a partner of the opposite sex, to stand facing each other, breathing in a relaxed way and looking into each other's eyes.

"Feel whatever emotions or sensations this connection may stir in you," I suggest. "You may feel nervousness, even fear, or you may feel excitement as you notice that you feel attracted. Keep breathing, looking and allowing."

With this first, tentative step, the world of Tantra starts to open up, because now two opposite energies are being invited to meet, and this meeting of polarities – however superficial it may be at the beginning – contains the whole alchemy of Tantra.

Tantra can be defined as the meeting of male and female polarities to create a dynamic, pulsating energy that carries you beyond the male-female duality into a state of oneness with existence.

"Even though it's something you're not used to, allow this person to see into you as deeply as possible. Just by looking, without turning away, you can receive this person, inviting them in through your eyes," I suggest.

One thing that's difficult for me to convey, in written form, is the tone and quality of my voice as I guide people through these exercises. It's second nature to me now, and it's not something I trained myself to do in any particular way, but I'm aware that it's a key element in my work – especially in a Tantra workshop where an atmosphere of trust has to be swiftly established and time is limited.

I remember, back in the late Sixties, a Canadian sociologist called Marshal McLuhan rocketed to fame in the United States and Europe for a single enigmatic statement that somehow conveyed the feeling of those times – and still applies today.

Commenting on a global culture dominated by the media and especially by television, McLuhan said, "The medium is the message."

I guess that's true of my voice in this workshop. It's inviting, encouraging and reassuring. It helps people understand that nothing bad is going to happen here, that we are all moving into this process with loving intention. My voice carries a blend of adventure, support and sensuality, with a little tickle in it, too. And somehow it also contains my thirty years of experience in working with people.

My voice is a big part of how I accomplish my work.

"Okay, give a namaste to this person with whom you have shared these few moments, and start walking around the room again."

The namaste, as I mentioned in the previous chapter, is the traditional form of greeting and departing in India, done with hands raised in front of your heart, palms pressed together. It carries the meaning, "I salute the divine in you," and I like to use it in my Tantra work, because it adds a flavor of respect and dignity to whoever gives or receives it.

I guide the participants into meeting another member of the opposite sex through the eyes and then, with the third meeting, I ask them to connect through the hands.

"Close your eyes and let your hands say 'hello' to each other in some gentle way. Make it a very soft touch, hardly any movement at all, just some way to indicate that you're here, that you're alive and willing to connect.

"As you hold hands, take a deep breath into your chest, into the area around your heart. Our hands are extensions of our hearts, because it is through them we give and receive. You may feel that your two hearts are connecting through your hands, through this touch."

People often start to cry when they do this exercise – when they suddenly begin to feel a heart connection through the hands. It creates a new level of sensitivity, and this is what we need in order to approach each other without being startled, scared, or shocked.

If we want to reach the heart of the Tantric experience we have to move slowly, gently, lovingly, so that trust is created, so that the delicate flower of Tantra can begin to open.

"Open your eyes and see this person," I invite them.

With hands and eyes connecting, energy starts to flow more strongly between partners and I keep encouraging them to allow – if they can – the other person to see them as deeply as possible.

"Be aware what might be preventing the energy from flowing between you. It may be experienced as tension in the shoulders, or the back of the neck, or maybe a kind of hardening in the eyes. It could be a kind of spacing out in the eyes, not really being here, or looking between the eyes so that meeting is avoided.

"Remember: this is a place, this is a space, where you can let some of these protections go, because it is a safe space. No one is going to jump on you, no one is going to cling to you. You can be open, you can give yourself this experience and it doesn't mean that anything further needs to happen between you."

In guiding people into an exercise, I am not trying to give everyone the same experience. What they feel, as they look and touch each other, varies widely, from fear to love, from tears to smiles.

As I see it, Tantra doesn't need uniformity. It needs people to bring awareness to whatever they are experiencing – it may be energy flowing in a certain way, a sensation inside the body, a feeling like anxiety or pleasure.

Once people's attention is focused on what is happening, here and now, inside themselves, they have the opportunity to recognize it, allow it and accept it. And acceptance is a golden Tantric key, because whenever reality is recognized and accepted, energy begins to move and flow.

All that is needed is to notice what *is*, and allow it. Everybody in the room may be experiencing something different, but if all these energies are accepted, then a group dynamic starts to happen, a Tantric river of energy starts to flow, heading for the ocean.

In my experience, and in the vision of both Reich and Osho, there is an ocean of energy in which we all exist as living organisms; there is a sea that surrounds us, that flows within us, that flows in and out of us, and this is the sea of life. We tune in to this ocean simply by 'feeling our feeling' and riding the wave of energy that moves from this point.

Naturally, we must begin this process where people are, which is on the periphery, on the outside, in social mode. The periphery is what is accessible; it's what people know, and where they are willing to start, just like this: standing in this room, holding hands with a partner, looking into each other's eyes.

"When you meet in this way, through the eyes and heart, you start to feel how you can look into almost anybody's heart," I explain. "We are all human; we all share the same longings, the same frailties. There is nothing to hide. See if you can allow this to happen. Let yourself be touched." Some people giggle, wipe away a tear, or smile with delight.

My Tantric work is an interesting dance: helping people to identify with our common humanness, while at the same time helping them to feel the polar difference between man and woman.

It's the oneness that creates trust and relaxation. It's the polarity that creates excitement, and I'm constantly inter-weaving these two qualities.

The atmosphere in the room is gradually changing as people start to relax and breathe more freely. Breathing is an important indicator of energy flow.

When people open their eyes in front of a new partner, it almost always happens that they stop breathing. I can hear it – I can hear, suddenly, not a breath is being taken in the room.

Then I say, "Notice if you've stopped breathing." Immediately, they all realize what has happened and I can hear people breathing again.

From experience, I can feel when there is a general rigidity and also when things become looser – when energy starts to flow, when people start to enjoy themselves.

Each time the participants connect with a new partner, things relax a little bit more, so usually, by the time they have met three or four people, they are becoming more grounded, trusting the group process.

Really, it's quite surprising. Given that people don't know each other and are nervous, it's remarkable how much warmth starts to flow around the room in such a short time.

Two more exercises that I introduce early in Tantra workshops are the Pelvic Swing and Hands Breathing, both of which are described earlier in this book. But, as I said before, it's a little different when such exercises are done in a Tantric context, with opposite sex partners.

The sex and heart centers are key areas when exploring energy, especially when we start to work with subtle Tantric meditations. We will be circling energy between these two centers, and they need to be alive, sensitive, ready for the challenge.

Introducing the Pelvic Swing, I ask men and women to stand facing each other, a couple of feet apart, making eye contact as they exhale together with a forward thrust of the pelvis, then swinging the pelvis back on the inhale.

While they are awakening the sex center in this way, I am talking about how much we are conditioned against it, how much we have been told not to go there.

"Now we're going to go there – just because they say, 'Don't go there!'" I joke, while guiding people into the exercise.

I also explain how necessary it is to generate this energy, to come alive at the level of the body, at the level of our basic vitality, because this is going to be our pump, our energy source as we move upwards through the body.

"We need to get this chakra alive," I tell the group. "We need to get our animal nature moving, accepting it, showing it to each other through the eyes, saying, 'Hey, look! I'm an alive animal!'"

In the same way, Hands Breathing energizes the heart center and here, too, opposite sex partnering gives an extra sparkle. It is the heart that gives us the quality of acceptance, plus the longing to give and receive. Without these three qualities, Tantric exploration would not get very far.

At this stage of the workshop, participants have awakened their energy and come closer to each other. Now it's time a get a little more intimate, but before doing so I explain that my approach to Tantra is not just about bodies meeting in sexual embrace.

We are interested in exploring subtle layers of energy, subtle qualities of feeling, so I ask people not to make love over the next five days in order to suspend old habit patterns, old sexual games, and be open to new layers of experience.

Generally speaking, this request is welcomed and honored by participants. Many feel relieved, because it takes the pressure off and removes concerns about finding and keeping a suitable partner.

With this settled, I invite men and women to pair up for a massage session – an easy way to become familiar with giving and receiving. Any structure involving the male-female dynamic is going to stimulate the polarity of attraction, and I want to encourage this in a friendly way, with some gentle touching.

I guide them into massaging the back of their partner, which is one of the most non-threatening parts of the body. The main emphasis is to loosen and relax muscles on either side of the spine, keeping the massage light and non-intrusive.

A back massage brings awareness to the spine as a powerful conductor of energy, connecting our roots in the earth with the cosmic, the beyond. One of Tantra's most important maps uses the spine to join our animal nature with the divine through a chain of seven chakras – I'll talk more about it in the next chapter.

I emphasize a non-doing quality in the touch because many people, when told to give a massage, immediately get busy, working hard, digging into the muscles, almost getting out of breath from effort.

When this happens, the one who is giving the massage disconnects from his own energy, because he's too involved in ideas about 'how to do it,' or 'how to please my partner' – also a common pattern in love-making. And when the giver is not connected with his own energy, there's no chance of connecting

196

with the energy of the receiving partner, so I keep reminding everyone that it's not about 'doing.' It's about being together in a space of relaxation.

I suggest they also explore massage at an energy level by making a few hand passes along the length of the spine, from the buttocks to the neck, keeping the hand an inch or two above the skin. This movement supports a sense of rising energy, an upward flow from earth to sky.

After the massage, the next step takes place as an evening session, when people are pleasantly relaxed, and when the lights can be dimmed to create a soft, intimate atmosphere. This is a Tantric meditation in which partners will experience several stages that help them to come closer, slowly falling in tune with each other energetically.

I ask everyone to choose a partner, then sit together on a mat, facing each other, not touching, eyes closed. When they are sitting comfortably, I guide them into belly breathing, because connecting with your own energy is an essential first step in any Tantric meeting between two people.

After a while, I invite them to open their eyes and look with a soft gaze into the eyes of their partner, hands lightly joined, spending a few minutes breathing and looking, meeting and connecting. As background, I play soft, meditative music.

This introductory stage of the exercise ends with a namaste, in which participants acknowledge and bow down to the buddha in front of them, reminding everyone that this is a meditation.

Now I ask them to turn around and sit back-to-back with the partner, so their spines are touching, then close their eyes. I invite them to focus attention on the back, using it as a way of connecting with the partner, feeling the partner's back through their own, feeling the partner's breathing, warmth, energy – all coming through the back.

After a few minutes, I invite them to gently sway together, eyes still closed, once again emphasizing that this is not a 'doing.' I want them to get used to the idea of allowing energy to flow by itself, rather than trying to control it.

It doesn't take long for energy to start rising up the spine, spreading warmth through the back, connecting with the partner's energy and beginning to merge. Swaying is a centering technique, so my invitation is to allow the energy to merge while remaining in your own center, not getting lost in trying to figure out what the partner is doing or thinking.

Now people are ready for a deeper meeting, so I slowly bring this stage of the exercise to an end, asking them to open their eyes, turn around and explore a new position, with an embrace that allows the front side of their bodies to meet.

This is the basic position I use for all front-to-front Tantric meetings, so it is worth describing in detail.

In the sitting position, facing each other, each partner raises and bends the right knee, keeping the foot on the mat. The left leg lies outstretched on the mat. When both partners do this, they can move towards each other, with the left leg sliding under the partner's right leg, until the front of their bodies touch.

In this way, it is possible to have physical contact that includes the pubic area, stomach and chest – a full-frontal embrace that at the same time is comfortable and relaxing. I also ask them to gently wrap their arms around each other, leaning forward slightly, so that their heads are side by side, cheek by cheek.

Since this is the first time participants are coming together in this way, I am not going to focus on the sex center, or do anything complicated, but simply invite them to bring awareness to their breathing, and to the breathing of their partner, tuning into each other's rhythm.

This sounds simple and innocent enough, as indeed it is, but it can also be a very intimate experience, because breathing together, finding a rhythm together, brings people very close, especially when the breath is slow and soft. It's a delicate experience requiring cooperation and empathy. Even making love doesn't necessarily bring people this close – like everything else, sex can be a habitual, mechanical activity.

I let this meeting continue for about ten minutes, supporting it with soft music, and then, as a slight variation, I invite partners to explore what it feels like to 'breathe through the heart,' focusing attention on the fourth chakra while still breathing in rhythm together. I don't mention polarities, or giving and receiving energy, but merely focusing awareness, to see how it feels to be 'in the heart' together.

Bringing the exercise to a close, I ask the partners to separate slowly, enough to be able to see each other, and spend a couple of minutes again looking into each other's eyes. Then, after some time, I guide them to separate completely and sit on their own, eyes closed, still facing each other but not touching.

This moment of aloneness is also important, allowing each individual to look inside and check what has happened to his or her energy after such an intimate meeting.

The exercise ends with a namaste.

It must be obvious by now that my focus in Tantric Pulsation is not so much on the physical body, but on exploring energy – how it flows, how it moves, how it can meet, melt and merge with another person's energy and separate again.

As I see it, many valuable things can be learned about sexual energy without becoming overtly sexual. Moreover, my Reichian background makes me aware that focusing on genitals and sexual arousal – kissing, touching, stimulating, turning on – can easily become mechanical and also very threatening, because there is so much emotional wounding around people's sexuality.

Women, especially, have insecurities, fears and a sense of protectiveness regarding the sex center and genitals. They don't want to be touched so intimately by strangers. Unless this is done by a lover, there is a ninety-nine percent chance that a woman's boundaries will be over-stepped and instead of opening up, her energy will shut down.

My approach is to orient Tantra toward people who may never have done any experiments with sexual energy and yet who can, within a few days, find themselves in a melting Tantric embrace – precisely because the approach is safe and non-threatening.

Chapter Fifteen

Exploring the Chakras

"Energy is eternal delight," said William Blake, the English romantic poet and mystic.

If he had lived a couple of hundred years later, and by chance we met, I would say to him, "Yes, William, you are right. But remember, energy is only delightful if it is allowed to move. If it gets stuck, your 'eternal' delight won't last five minutes."

I would also point out that the chances of experiencing delight in one's life are directly proportional to the freedom with which energy can move through the human body.

Poets and artists like Blake enjoy only brief glimpses of peak experiences and have no control over how and when they occur – that is their anguish – unless, like Coleridge, they turn to drugs to give them the longed-for 'high.'

But ecstasy, delight and other desirable states need not be so rare in human experience. Nor need we be a special type of person – poet or artist – to enjoy them. As I indicated in a previous chapter, I have been fortunate enough to experience these things many times in my own life, and I do not regard myself as more gifted or extraordinary than anyone else.

Fundamentally, it is a question of accessing one's own energy, removing the blocks that inhibit it, and allowing it to flow. Once energy is available and moving, its potential can be explored in thousands of creative ways: dancing, singing, playing a musical instrument, meditating, celebrating, working, making love.... The possibilities are endless.

It's really not a question of what one does, but the feeling of totality and aliveness with which one does it – and aliveness depends on energy in motion.

In my work, this movement of energy has two basic directions of flow. The first part of the journey, the de-armoring process, follows a downward path through the segments, from the head down to the pelvis. In the second part, the awakened energy naturally begins to overflow from the sex center and starts to rise up through the body, through the seven chakras.

I first learned about chakras back in the early Seventies, when I was living in San Francisco and reading books published by the Theosophical Society, an esoteric organization that enjoyed its heyday in India and Europe at the beginning of the twentieth century, and which still exists today.

One of the society's founders, Charles Leadbeater, wrote a book on the chakras which became an all-time esoteric best-seller, and that was the one I read. There wasn't much else published in those days, except translations from Hindu scriptures that to me were completely incomprehensible.

After I started training with the Kelleys in their Radix work, I came to understand that the seven chakras are located in the same areas of the body as the seven Reichian segments.

The emotional release work was provoking a lot of sensations in my body and sometimes I would feel energy centers vibrating – particularly in the solar plexus and heart, which correspond to the third and fourth chakras.

I did not see spinning disks of energy, or rainbow colors, but when my heart was touched I would feel the energy pulsating in the center of my chest, and I'd know that this was my fourth chakra opening.

The more I worked with the segments, the more I understood that when the energy starts to move, becoming alive and sensitive, it opens inwards, towards a core energetic experience.

As I see it, the muscular segments described by Reich form the outer layers of the chakras – the segments constitute the physical part, inside which are layers and layers of more subtle energies.

To me, chakras are doorways into oneself, doorways into different qualities of human energy. There is one life-force, one life-energy, flowing through our entire system, and when it vibrates through a particular chakra, or expresses in a particular segment, it has certain qualities connected with specific issues. I have mentioned some of these issues in previous chapters, but I think it's worth presenting a more comprehensive list here to give an overview of the chakra system.

First Chakra: Life Center

The first chakra is located deep within the pelvis and, in Reichian terms, within the pelvic segment. It is connected to the organs of the pelvic region, including the genitals, anus and bladder.

This energy center, also called the 'root chakra,' reaches energetically into the legs and feet, grounding us on the earth. Here we are in touch with our animal nature – all that is primitive and uncivilized.

The first chakra rules the physical body, including reproduction, health or sickness, strength or weakness, the capacity of the body to take us through life, to make a living, to survive. Most of man's existence on this planet has been lived through the first chakra, especially before the dawn of civilization, when food, sex and shelter were overriding issues.

This chakra connects us with our sexuality and all of the experiences we have around this basic issue: infantile sexuality, the innocence and pleasurable nature of those experiences; adolescent sexuality, which is full of uncertainty, moods, shakiness and shyness, a time when we're trying things out, making mistakes, getting rejected – all of these things.

Second Chakra: Feeling Center

The second chakra is found in the belly and governs the Reichian abdominal segment, including the intestines and also the womb. As we have seen, the belly is the source of many deep feelings and emotions, especially those focused on the mother – because of the proximity of the umbilical cord to this center when we were in the womb.

All of our needs, our dependence on other people, our relationships, are ruled from here, including a sense of tribal community and collective identity.

This chakra is also connected with sensuality, with enjoying movement and sensation in the body, and is responsible for the pleasure we experience in melting and merging energetically with another person while making love.

For this reason, a major issue of the second chakra is co-dependency, which has its origins in the mother-child relationship. This dynamic involves the tension between the need to merge with another person and the need to retain a sense of autonomy and individuality.

Third Chakra: Power Center

The third chakra is located in the diaphragm segment, the solar plexus, and is the center of fire, expression and assertion. It also contains a number of important organs, including the liver, stomach, spleen and pancreas.

It is traditionally called the power center, because this is where our conflicts with other people originate. Here we assert the feeling of 'I' as a separate individual and as a higher value than the collective 'we' of the second chakra.

Judgment, evaluation and discrimination have their roots in this center, as well as comparison, competition, the polarities of inferiority and superiority, feeling better than or not as good as others, feeling stronger or weaker. Here, too, we experience the freedom of being a unique individual.

Fourth Chakra: Love Center

The fourth chakra is located in the center of the chest, or thoracic segment, between the breasts. It rules both the physical and emotional heart and, like the belly, is a major feeling center.

This chakra is connected with our capacity to love, to share with others, and our longing to commune with other human beings in an unconditional way that is beyond the ego-centered differences of the third chakra.

When we are rejected in love, this is where the wound is felt and stored. We carry hurt feelings and emotional wounds in the fourth chakra, from those times when we were not accepted, when we could not get the love we longed to receive from another.

The heart is a bridge between three chakras below and three above. The first three chakras are rooted in our animal nature – the physical, the instinctual. When we come to the heart we move from animal to human and towards the divine.

Fifth Chakra: Expression Center

The fifth chakra is located in the throat, but is connected with two Reichian segments, the cervical and the oral, so in this way the mouth becomes an extension of the fifth chakra.

This chakra governs our creativity and all kinds of expression, including language. Experiences of the four lower centers are coded, or stored, in the fifth chakra as beliefs, expectations, concepts – the creation of a Weltanschauung, or world view that governs our way of looking at life.

The throat chakra possesses the quality of spontaneity, the ability to step out of fixed forms and ideas into something new, and give it creative expression. Conversely, a blocked throat center can result in a rigid, inflexible set of beliefs.

In its receptive mode, this chakra is connected with taking in what is nourishing for us – not only in terms of food, but also ideas, energy and feelings.

Sixth Chakra: Awareness Center

The sixth chakra, also referred to as the third eye, is located in the forehead, between and slightly above the eyebrows. It includes the Reichian ocular segment.

This chakra is connected with awareness and understanding, the capacity to see things clearly and accurately. It is associated with psychic and intuitive powers, which are also a kind of 'seeing.'

When open and vibrating with energy, this chakra can give an experience of unlimited inner space – the awareness that human consciousness and energy are not confined to the body/mind mechanism.

When we experience bliss – an expansive and ecstatic quality, similar to love, that is not addressed to anyone or anything specific – it arises from this center.

Seventh Chakra: Cosmic Center

The seventh chakra is located at the top of the head, the crown of the skull. Technically speaking, the top of the head is included in the Reichian ocular segment, but this chakra exists beyond the world of issues, or even definition.

Not much can be said about this chakra, because it is also beyond the realm of concepts and language. Fundamentally, it is a spiritual experience of oneness, union with the divine, a state of wholeness and harmony with existence that is beyond duality.

After describing the chakras in my Tantric Pulsation workshops, I offer participants a taste of how they can invite energy to move through these centers.

For this, I introduce a powerful meditation technique called 'Chakra Breathing' that uses a combination of sound, breathing and movement to energize the seven chakras, beginning with the sex center.

Chakra Breathing has been, for me, an all-time favorite and a personal key for my understanding of the chakras and how they function.

The meditation is based on a Sufi technique, in which a group of people breathe together, making deep, slow sounds that resonate in the lowest chakra. They gradually increase the speed and intensity of their breathing, using higher tones as they move up the chakras, vibrating in one center after the other.

Similar versions of this technique are available from a variety of sources, but I like the Sufi way of doing it, because it's very dynamic and alive. If you fall in tune with the rhythm of the breathing, you learn how to create a kind of 'popping-in' effect with each sound that is very effective for entering each of the chakras, energizing them and shaking them up.

Chakra Breathing is done in the grounded stance – standing, with shoulders relaxed, knees slightly bent, eyes closed – and breathing through a relaxed, open mouth.

I explain to the group that we are going to breathe into each chakra in turn, moving from first to seventh, culminating in a crescendo-like peak that reminds me of the Reichian orgasm formula.

As we move up through the chakras, the sounds that we make will naturally become higher, but they are not fixed to any particular tone – it is left to each individual to find the right sound that allows him, or her, to feel each chakra vibrating.

We begin by breathing slowly and making a deep sound that vibrates right down in the sex center. At the same time, I invite participants to use their inner vision, perhaps imagining a ball of energy in the first chakra, filling like a balloon each time we breathe into this center, deflating as we breathe out, pulsating rhythmically in the pelvis.

We also add a hip movement. As the breath enters through the mouth, penetrating down to the first chakra, we swing the pelvis back. As we breathe out, we swing the pelvis forward, and this helps to create a low sound – you might call it a grunt.

In this way, we vibrate the sex center with sound, breathing, movement and visualization simultaneously. For about a minute, to a minute-and-a-half, we breathe like this into the first chakra.

A bell rings and we bring our awareness to the second chakra, in the lower belly, visualizing the breath moving strongly into this area, while making a grunting sound – now a little bit higher in tone – that will vibrate at this point.

We imagine that the ball of energy has also moved up into the lower belly, still expanding and contracting with the inhale and exhale.

The pelvis continues to swing with the breathing throughout the exercise, serving like a pump that keeps vital energy flowing up through the body, while at the same time keeping us grounded, connected to the earth.

In this way, we continue up through the chakras. When we come up to the fourth chakra and start to breathe here, we involve the whole rib cage, arms, and shoulders in movement. In fact, all the way up, I ask people to move muscles within the body that are surrounding each chakra, helping to focus attention on each segment and fill it with vitality.

For example, at the fourth chakra, people sometimes put their hands close to the chest with the in-breath, then push out in front of them with the out-breath – it's up to each individual to discover how best to express the energy.

When we reach the sixth chakra, or third eye, the sound is very high, which is necessary in order to vibrate this area of the body. You can experiment with this yourself – a deep sound just doesn't vibrate here. The hands are moving close to the forehead and the pelvis is still pumping away....

At the seventh chakra, the sound is almost a squeak, very high-pitched, and the hands are used to shoot the energy out of the top of the head, giving it to the universe.

After reaching the seventh, we reverse the pattern and, more quickly now, breathe all the way back down through the chakras – sliding down, bringing the sound down as we go – so that when we arrive back in the first chakra we again have a deep sound.

There are three cycles of breathing, moving up the chakras and down again, each cycle taking about ten minutes. At the end, we sit silently for ten or fifteen minutes just to feel and acknowledge all the energy that has been generated – which, by the way, is a lot. It's a very powerful meditation.

Chakra Breathing opens up energies in each individual chakra and makes them more accessible. After people have done the meditation several times, they can experience a feeling of unity among all the chakras, a sense of energy flowing up and down the spine, a sense of integration in the energy system as a whole.

I find this technique helpful in mobilizing energies in all the Reichian segments, which we can then work with in a variety of ways, among them emotional release and Tantric couple work.

Chakra Energy Exploration

Taking the chakra work deeper, the room is arranged so that all participants have a mat to lie on, and for the next hour I guide them through an exercise called Chakra Energy Exploration. Now that the chakras have been charged with energy, I want to encourage people to investigate each one in more depth.

I picture the chakras as doorways for the expression of different qualities of human energy. Just as light breaks down into the seven rainbow colors, so each chakra focuses life energy through a different 'lens,' from the most simple and lowest vibration in the first chakra, to the highest, most subtle and complex in the sixth and seventh.

When we consciously enter and bring our awareness to a particular chakra, we can meet the issues contained and expressed there. This exploration exercise works simultaneously on the physical segments and on the mental-emotional issues that have accumulated in these areas.

We begin in the basic breathing position, lying on our backs on a mat, knees raised and bent, feet flat on the floor.

First, we build up a charge of energy, breathing into the belly, then gradually expanding our focus to include the diaphragm and chest.

I explain that in this exercise we're going to enter into each chakra by visualizing its position in the body, breathing into this place, letting sounds come from the throat and mouth, and, as the exploration proceeds, allowing the body to move spontaneously in whatever way the energy suggests.

I guide them into the first chakra, reminding them of some of the issues I talked about in my introduction. I suggest that here people may connect with past sexual experiences or sexual traumas. They may also get in touch with raw animal energies, animal desires that want sex, want food, and want it now – a kind of immediate, lusty physicality that lives here in the first chakra.

I invite them to move this part of the body, so they may be wriggling or bouncing the pelvis, swaying their legs, stamping their feet. If they are coming in contact with animal energy they may be growling, roaring, showing their teeth, turning their hands into claws.

As this exploration goes deeper, people often connect with negative feelings like anger. It's primitive, noisy, and I use loud music to encourage expression – African drumming works well in the first chakra.

It's also possible that memories will pop up, in the form of thoughts or pictures, associated with sexual and animal issues. I suggest to the participants that they can work with these pictures, saying things like, "I want it!...Give it to me!...It's mine!...Fuck off!"

We're not just dealing with negative emotions – the first chakra can also be enjoyed and experienced as a celebration of pure physical aliveness and animal vitality. Some people may not feel very much here; they come in contact with a kind of deadness. This response can be found in any of the chakras, which may indicate strong blocking or repression in this area.

This, too, is a valuable discovery. It simply shows an area where they can work to bring more aliveness – perhaps some Reichian de-armoring is needed.

We explore the first chakra for seven or eight minutes and then, without stopping at the second chakra, I guide them into the third, the power center, because both the first and third chakras represent strong, outgoing, expressive energies.

At the beginning of the exploration, I explained that we will begin by working with the outward-directed energies – the first and third – and then, when these strong energies have been expressed, we will explore the second and fourth chakras, which are more inward-directed and receptive.

I remind people that the third chakra is where our conflicts play themselves out, where our competitive feelings, our fighting feelings, are activated. This is our fire center, from where an assertion of 'I' emerges that can be very empowering, feeling one's own strength and independence.

Participants may discover weakness rather than strength, and memories of emotional collapse – feelings like, "I can't manage, I can't do it."

Again, I encourage them to use words, remembering specific conflicts with others, saying things that need to be said, moving their bodies to emphasize their emotions.

They may be pounding their arms on the mat, shouting with anger, crying out of weakness, perhaps even beating their chests like big, male gorillas to announce their power and dominance.

After the third chakra has been investigated, we drop down to the belly, the second chakra, which contains a very different and much softer kind of energy.

Playing gentle music, I invite them to breathe in here, feel in here.

As we enter the world of the belly, many people immediately start to cry, especially when I mention mother issues, reminding them of when they were small babies – how much they needed the mother's love, care, warmth, nourishment and support.

People may also have a positive experience, remembering the cozy maternal energy that gave a feeling of safety and security, but this is also where we carry wounds of abandonment, when we didn't get what we needed, or when the mother left.

I also mention how feelings connected with the mother play out in our later relationships with boyfriends and girlfriends, husbands, wives and lovers, creating demands and attitudes like:

"Now that you are my girlfriend/boyfriend you have to be my mommy/daddy."

"I need you so much; if you leave me I will die."

These are carry-over feelings from childhood. It's not that we will actually die if the lover leaves, but it often feels like it because of early traumatic experiences.

From the belly, we move to the fourth chakra, the heart, which contains a soft type of energy similar to that of the second. This is where we care about other people. In the heart we discover our longing to share with others, our feelings of love, of wanting to give whatever we have.

In the heart, too, we have acquired armoring around wounds of rejection and unfulfilled longings, manifesting as hurt, sadness and tears. It is also from the heart that we can forgive those who have hurt us, or ask forgiveness from those whom we have hurt. I mention these things as triggers to help release suppressed emotion.

The hands are extensions of the heart and I invite people to reach out, maybe to someone, perhaps holding a pillow that represents a person, speaking words from the heart that long to be expressed.

The fourth chakra can also be very joyful as people connect with the heart's tremendous capacity to expand with love, radiating this healing energy, including the whole world in its loving embrace.

After we've been in the heart for some time, I ask the participants to sit up and find a comfortable position with a straight spine. This is helpful for exploring the upper three chakras, connecting with a rising movement of energy that takes us beyond the animal, even beyond the human.

I guide people into the fifth, sixth and seventh chakras, where they may discover a sense of spaciousness, a clear inner sky. This is where human consciousness starts to feel free, where we can experience the unlimited sense of an open sky within us.

It will be different for everyone, but I know that almost all of the participants will be able to feel a sense of expanding energy, rising upwards, going beyond the finite boundaries of the body, connecting with what is divine in us, with some quality of 'the beyond,' with a sense of oneness.

It's important that, in this higher state of consciousness, we do not forget to ground the experience, so I remind people that this divineness needs to be anchored in the physical body – they are two polarities of a continuum between animal and spirit. Both polarities are needed for the total experience of being human.

Playing meditative flute music, I again guide people from the base of the spine all the way up through the chakras, emphasizing the rainbow of colors we meet on the journey, finally entering the clear blue sky of inner space.

To conclude, I play a quote of Osho in which he talks about the importance of having both roots and wings: roots that go deep into the earth, to keep us grounded in the body, and wings to fly through the inner sky to the beyond that beckons the human spirit. Embracing this polarity gives us a sense of wholeness.

At this point in our Tantric journey we have left Reich behind, because although he talked about sexual gratification, physical happiness and even love, the blissfulness of meditation really wasn't in his vocabulary. He addresses the animal and the human, but never acquired a clear sense of anything beyond them.

Reich explored the cosmic dimension, in the sense that he talked about orgone energy filling all space, and developed theories about galaxy formation through the dynamics of 'cosmic superimposition' – a force which also underlies our planetary weather formations that spiral around centers of low and high pressure.

But he talked as a physicist, not as a mystic. I am sure he was often in awe at the profound nature of what he was discovering, but his condemnatory view of religion – as a major oppressor of the human spirit – may well have prevented him from exploring the spiritual dimension.

In several of his discourses, Osho talks fondly of Reich, saying that, had he lived in India or the East, he would have become enlightened.

The work we do with the chakras, both the breathing technique and the exploration exercise, has a deep effect on most Tantric Pulsation participants, and I encourage them to stay in silence when they leave the room.

In the following session, everyone is provided with paper and crayons, and I invite them to draw their experiences, illustrating the shape, color and expression of their energy as it moved through the chakras. This gives them an opportunity to integrate the experience.

The Chakra Energy Exploration is a vehicle to go on an inner adventure, making discoveries, making the hidden visible, and I support people to process their experiences by painting, drawing, sharing with others, writing in their notebooks...seeing how these new experiences can fit with their lives.

Although this group process is a tremendous support, each person's experience is going to be unique. The inner journey is essentially a solo flight, from the alone to the alone. Even in the deepest, most intimate Tantric embrace with a partner, it is one's own inner experience that remains the absolute criterion.

This may feel like a cold shower for those romantic souls who long for permanent union with the beloved, but understanding one's essential aloneness is an important foundation stone for meditation.

It's also a good preparation for moving into the next dimension of the Tantra journey: the dynamics of male and female energies, and the circle of light that can make them one.

Chapter Sixteen

The Circle of Light

"Me Tarzan. You Jane."

It has been a long, long time since Johnny Weissmuller, American athlete turned actor, uttered these immortal words, wowing movie audiences around the world with his portrayal of Tarzan, Lord of the Jungle.

Many other actors, before and since, have played the charismatic, tree-hopping hero created by Edgar Rice Burroughs – there have been 45 movies featuring Tarzan spanning eighty years of silver screen history – but almost everyone agrees that nobody did it quite like Johnny.

Teaming up with Maureen O'Sullivan, the breathtakingly beautiful Irish actress who played Jane Parker, Weissmuller somehow captured the essence of masculinity for a generation of movie goers in the 1930's and '40's.

Tarzan and Jane never made love on screen. In fact, after a daring underwater nude dance in their second movie, 'Tarzan and His Mate,' the sexual chemistry between Weissmuller and O'Sullivan was deliberately diluted so that their box office appeal could be extended to include family audiences, kids and all.

But when Tarzan cupped a hand to his mouth and uttered his famous jungle cry, 'Aaahuuaahuuaaah!' Jane could smile in the knowledge that her man was on his way back to their tree-top love nest for another night of off-screen passion.

She also knew that if she got into trouble – cannibals, giant apes and hungry crocodiles were just some of the hazards a young woman might encounter while strolling through the jungle –

Tarzan would come swinging down out of the trees, sweep her off her feet, sling her over his shoulder and carry her away to safety.

Male and female stereotypes have shifted quite a bit since the days of Weissmuller and O'Sullivan. Women have asserted their freedom from conventional roles such as wife, mother, housekeeper and cook, entering into many areas of society that were predominantly male – for example, politics, business and sport.

Naturally, our movies reflect the changing trends. Helpless females are an increasingly rare species. These days, if you're having an on-screen crisis, you're as likely to be rescued by Charlie's Angels as by a he-man in a tux.

All well and good, but liberation has brought its share of confusion to both genders. Women who fight their way to the top of a man's world don't necessarily feel happier because of it. Men who try to be soft, sympathetic and understanding all too frequently encounter the "nice guys finish last" syndrome while watching the woman of their dreams walk off with Mr. Macho.

When I jetted off to India in the mid-Seventies I ducked out of the ongoing gender debate in the US and found myself in a commune of men and women where something very different was going on.

Osho, in his discourses, was emphasizing the importance of gender differences. He was saying that, as far as sex, love and Tantra are concerned, men and women need to be as different as possible. In other words, a man needs to be a man, and a woman needs to be a woman.

What are the basic gender differences? Such lists can be long, but here are a few qualities relevant to Tantra.

Masculine qualities: active, energetically moving outwards, adventurous, rational, providing and protecting. Bodies tend to be angular and hard.

Feminine qualities: receptive, energetically moving inwards, nest-building, intuitive, nurturing and embracing. Bodies tend to be soft and round.

The natural universe that surrounds us is essentially a dance of energy between such polar opposites. Day and night, summer and winter, male and female, positive and negative, ebb and flow.... Energy needs to move, and the stronger the polarities, the greater the charge of energy that can flow between them.

In the world of Tantra, this has clear implications. A feminine type of man and a masculine type of woman, coming together in love-making, are unlikely to be able to create a strong charge of energy. A man brimming over with testosterone and a soft, receptive woman have a better chance of dynamic chemistry, generating more charge, enjoying deeper orgasms.

This does not mean we need to return to the jungle with Johnny and Maureen. But it does suggest that we pay more attention to nature and less to politically fashionable ideas about gender merging.

However, Osho's vision of Tantra is multi-dimensional and can be easily misunderstood. His emphasis on sexual differences does not mean that women should be prevented from exploring their own male energy, or that men should not come to know their female side, their 'inner woman.'

On the contrary, in a week-long women's liberation group developed under his guidance, female participants spend three days dressing and behaving as men – just to become acquainted with the polar opposite inside themselves. A men's liberation group, based on similar guidelines, gives male participants the opportunity to spend three days as women.

And, as I mentioned before, when I was living in Osho's commune in Oregon, I worked in construction – a very physical, challenging, male activity – and loved every minute of it.

The invitation, as I understand Osho, is to experience everything, the full spectrum of male and female energy, while at the same time understanding the basic polarity of energy flow in the human body.

It's good for a woman to know her male qualities, and to be able to access them when needed, but it would be frustrating and self-defeating for her to give these qualities precedence over her predominantly female nature. The same goes for a man.

Energetically, as well as physically, a male body is configured very differently from a female body, and this difference needs to

217

be recognized if we are to enjoy and explore the potential for pleasure our bodies offer.

One of the most important things to understand is that the chakras in men and women are oppositely charged.

The first chakra in men is positively charged. This is obvious, because the sexual organ stands out from the body and the penis is designed to penetrate the woman's vagina. At her sex center, the woman is the negative pole, her sexual organ goes inward and is designed to receive the penis.

It is a self-evident, biological fact of life, and energy follows the physical design. It is not just semen that flows into the woman's body during sexual intercourse. The man's energy pours into the woman at this chakra.

That's why I was reminded of Tarzan and Jane when I began this chapter. The first chakra rules the physical body and the sex organs, and here a man needs to be a man, a woman needs to be a woman, and that's just the way it is.

In the second chakra, in the lower belly, the woman is positively charged and the man is negatively charged. Since this chakra governs emotion and feeling, it becomes clear why so many men are afraid of women's emotions – nature has put them on the receiving end of a strong, incoming energy and it can be a scary experience.

Just as a woman fears being overwhelmed by male sexual aggression at the first chakra, a man fears being overwhelmed by emotion at the second, especially when it takes the form of tears and tantrums.

It also explains why women need more foreplay than men before making love. A woman is basically seduced into sex through her second chakra. She needs to be wooed with chocolates, flowers, sensual caresses, sweet words and hugs, only then does her positively charged second chakra send a message to her negatively charged first chakra that it's okay to let the man in.

At the third chakra, the polarity again switches, with the man's energy becoming positive and the woman's negative. This is why men like to shout – for example, in stadiums at competitive sporting events. The sound resonates in the power center and gives a sense of strength. It also explains why men are more comfortable with anger than with tears.

At the fourth chakra, the polarity switches once more: the woman is positive, the man negative. It is not just milk that pours from a woman's breasts when she feeds her child. The love energy of the heart chakra goes with it, radiating outward and nourishing the child in an energetic way, making it feel wanted and cherished.

It takes courage for a man to receive a woman's love, because, in a way, he becomes a child again, receiving the woman's nourishing energy. And, of course, it explains man's fascination with the female breast – he has not forgotten how fulfilling it was to suckle there as a baby.

Above the fourth, polarization is not as strong, and at the seventh and last chakra all polarities merge into one.

One of the interesting effects of polarization is that, from the perspective of Tantra, it is possible to create circles of energy flowing between men and women, especially between the first and fourth chakras.

Before explaining how I guide people into experiencing these circles, I need to introduce an ancient Indian spiritual text called 'Vigyan Bhairav Tantra.' Translated, these three Sanskrit words mean 'techniques for going beyond consciousness,' an appropriate title because the sutras of this text contain no less than 112 methods of meditation.

The word 'Tantra,' in this context, does not indicate sexual techniques, although several are mentioned within the scripture. In ancient times, 'Tantra' simply meant 'method' or 'technique,' so Vigyan Bhairav Tantra is really a comprehensive list of all known meditation methods.

The scripture was compiled by enlightened mystics, whose names have been long forgotten. But, whoever they were, they were inclined towards a poetic and dramatic literary style, so they presented their techniques in the form of spiritual instruction, given by Lord Shiva to his consort Devi.

Devi asks Shiva questions, as a disciple would ask a spiritual master, and Shiva responds. But Devi is far more than just a disciple. She is Shiva's feminine half and his lover. In fact, the two are sometimes depicted as one, as in the statue of Shiva called 'Ardhanarishwar,' where he is shown as half man, half woman. So this is also a dialogue between two very intimate lovers.

In the early Seventies, Osho devoted many discourses to these dialogues, commenting on all 112 meditation methods and paying special attention to one that was designed specifically for women. He said it was a rare phenomenon because, as we all know, religion and spirituality in the past have been dominated almost exclusively by men.

Even when women were involved, such as the young female mediums who, under the influence of intoxicants, made utterances for the Oracle of Delphi in ancient Greece, they were controlled and manipulated by male priests.

So for the mystics of Vigyan Bhairav Tantra to have devised this method for women several thousand years ago – long before anyone had heard the words 'women's liberation' – is something of a minor miracle.

For this particular meditation technique, Shiva instructs Devi, "Feel the fine qualities of creativity permeating your breasts and assuming delicate configurations."

Commenting on this technique, Osho begins by defining the basic attraction between men and women as that of polar opposites. Energetically, he sees men and women as two electrical half-circuits, seeking completion through uniting in a loving embrace.

For a woman, the strongest positive pole in her body is located in the area of her breasts and this is why Shiva instructs Devi to focus her attention here. When a woman concentrates on the breasts in a relaxed and easy way, she will begin to feel a deep sweetness radiating out from this area, enveloping her whole body and pulsating around her like an aura.

Osho makes it clear that a man cannot do this meditation in exactly the same way as a woman. If a man concentrates on his breasts he may even start to feel uneasy, because in the male body this area is polarized negatively.

The man's strongest positive charge is located in the sex center, so if he wants to do this meditation he must focus his attention on the root of his penis. Here is where he expresses his positive qualities of strength and groundedness.

Expanding on Shiva's instruction to Devi, Osho says that the opposite polarities in male and female bodies create an opportunity for a circle of energy to happen between them. The man gives his energy at the first chakra, where the woman receives it and channels it up her spine, giving it back to the man through her breasts. He receives the energy in his chest and channels it down to his first chakra, giving it back to the woman again.

Such a circle of energy can happen spontaneously, in ordinary love-making, but it is rare because both partners need to be relaxed, open to each other, and in a meditative mood for the energy to flow.

In Tantric Pulsation, my aim is to give participants a solid experience of energy circling between the first and fourth chakras, because this is the easiest place to give people a taste of how Tantra works. This exercise is called 'The Circle of Light.'

First, I explain the male-female polarities and the opportunity this presents. Then I guide the group into Soft Pulsation with everyone lying down by themselves on a mat, in the basic breathing position, knees raised, feet on the floor. With each in-breath, the pelvis swings back, pressing the tailbone into the mat, and with each out-breath the pelvis rocks forward, lifting the genitals and tailbone off the mat.

When people find the pulsating rhythm of this movement it almost feels as if the pelvis is doing the breathing, bringing a flow of energy all the way down into the lower part of the body.

Once the breathing rhythm has been established, I ask men to rest their hands lightly on their genitals, and women to rest their hands lightly on their breasts – coming in contact with their strongest positive pole.

"Imagine that you can breathe out through this place, through the positive chakra," I suggest.

Gradually, as they go deeper into breathing, I invite them to let their hands express this outgoing movement of energy, moving away from the body on the out-breath, as if riding a wave that flows upward from this point. On the in-breath, the hands return to the body, resting gently on the positive pole as before.

After a few minutes, I invite them to complete the circle by breathing in through the receptive or negative pole.

For women, the full circle goes like this:

Women breathe out through their breasts, letting their hands move away from the body and then arcing in a semi-circle down towards the sex center, where they inhale, imagining as they do so that energy is entering the body here and traveling up the spine, arriving again at the breasts.

The men's circle:

Men breathe out through the sex center, letting their hands rise and make a semi-circle to the fourth chakra, then inhaling, imagining the energy is flowing in through the chest and down the spine, arriving again at the sex center.

Meanwhile, the movement of the pelvis continues for both sexes, keeping everyone grounded in the pelvis, generating energy. The exercise continues for a total of about thirty minutes, with members of each sex exploring how to make a circle of their own energy.

After a short break, I invite people to walk around the room, mingling with each other, choosing someone with whom they feel comfortable.

One of the most important qualities to develop in Tantra is the quality of receptivity. In my experience, being receptive is the more difficult half of the giving-receiving polarity, because to receive means you are taking someone else into your energy system. This requires trust – to let another person in.

I now introduce an exercise in pairs, in which the active partner explores giving with the quality of love, while the passive partner receives with the quality of trust.

Partners sit facing each other, beginning with a namaste and looking into each other's eyes. After a couple of minutes, I ask the men to close their eyes and allow themselves to slip into a mood of receptivity.

I invite the women to look with the eyes of love at the face of this man sitting in front of them, with a feeling of looking at a beloved – somebody they care about – and to allow this feeling to move towards the man as a flow of loving energy. The man allows this energy to wash over him, receiving from the woman.

I like to do it this way, with the woman in active mode first, because women have been trained to be on the receiving end, and inevitably have wounds around this issue. They've been taken advantage of, or not listened to – somehow not taken into account.

So I want to give them a chance to come out toward the man first, letting the man go into receptive mode, which is also a challenge for him, going against the grain of male conditioning.

I ask the women to take the hands of the man and let their loving energy flow from their hearts, down their arms and into the hands of their partner. Then, after a few minutes, to gradually and very softly begin to touch the man's face, caressing his skin with as much care and gentleness as they can.

It is not a massage, but more a caress; not so much a doing, more a presence, as if the woman's energy field can penetrate into the man's field and just send love.

Usually, during this stage, I have to remind the men a couple of times that there is nothing to do, because when men start to feel a woman's touch they think they have to respond in some way, by reaching out to the woman's hands, or resting a hand on the woman's knee – it's quite difficult for them to just receive.

I invite women to change their position, if they wish, to move around behind the man, or to the side, to continue touching in a loving, giving way, on the back of the head, neck, or shoulders.

After about fifteen minutes I bring this stage of the exercise to a close, asking the woman to come and sit again in front, facing the man, and for the man to open his eyes and look at the woman who has been giving to him.

Usually, this is a very touching moment. If the man has really allowed himself to receive, then opening the eyes can bring sweet tears of gratitude, with feelings like, "Oh, nobody has ever touched me like this, where I didn't have to do something in exchange for it...."

It just falls right into the heart.

Then I reverse the roles, with the women receiving and the men giving.

It is a beautiful exercise and I also use it in normal Pulsation groups, as an easy and simple way to relax and receive unfamiliar tenderness.

By this time, lunch break is upon us, and the invitation now is for the man and woman in each partnership to remain physically in contact for the whole time, while walking, sitting, eating, smoking…the only exception being when one wants to go to the bathroom. They are to have no contact with other people.

The purpose is to maintain the atmosphere of melting and merging energy that we have created during the morning session, so that we can carry it with us into the afternoon.

As with every exercise, people have different degrees of enjoyment and totality. Some partnerships break up immediately, because one of the partners just doesn't want to do it – feeling too confined or trapped. But most people give it their best shot and when everyone comes back after lunch I can see that the quality of melted energy has been sustained.

Keeping the same partner, the afternoon session is going to be spent bringing the man and woman together in the Circle of Light.

Sitting facing each other on the mat with their eyes closed, men and women rest their hands on their own positive pole and, breathing deeply, begin to create a circle of energy in themselves, as they did in the morning session.

The woman's hands arc in a semi-circle from her breasts down to the genitals on the out-breath, then slide back up her body to the breasts on the in-breath. The men's hands arc up from the genitals to the chest on the out-breath, then slide back down the body on the in-breath.

Even though they are not touching, and not looking at each other, the partners are already interacting energetically – just because they are facing each other.

As he exhales, the man's hands are moving away from his sex center out towards the woman's sex center. As she exhales, the woman's hands are moving out from her heart center towards the man's chest. They are not necessarily breathing in the same rhythm but a flow is beginning to be established.

I explain this dynamic to the participants and invite them to visualize that their partners are included in the circle of energy – now it is one circle moving between both

Now, even though her eyes are closed, the woman gives her energy from her breasts to the man, visualizing it going into his chest, down his spine and coming out of his sex center. She receives it in her own sex center and, breathing in deeply, channels it up her spine to her breasts.

The man does the same, giving from the first chakra, visualizing the energy moving up the woman's spine and then out through her breasts, receiving it in his chest.

After some time, I ask both partners to open their eyes and visually connect, continuing this movement of their hands and letting their breathing rhythms fall in tune. A kind of intimacy is beginning to happen as the circle becomes harmonious.

Eventually, I invite the pair to move into an embrace, using the position I have already described, while continuing to visualize the circle of energy flowing between them. Now the poles are physically touching and the energy can move more strongly, moving from the man's sex to the woman's sex, from the woman's breasts to the man's chest.

In the beginning, I suggest they breathe in the same rhythm so they can become familiar with the exercise and relax into the energy flow. Later, I suggest they may like to try a variation, with the man breathing in as the woman exhales, the man breathing out as the woman inhales.

But my priority is to keep things simple. I don't want people to lose contact with the energy through too much instruction and complicated visualization.

For the same reason, I don't emphasize physical movement, only a very slight swaying, because I want to stay away from the 'doing' aspect that can quickly develop into a kind of sexual humping. This is a natural tendency, to get the juices going, but there's also a big danger of switching to performance instead of sensory experience, cutting off the energy.

The partners spend about fifteen minutes in this embrace and then I ask them to slowly separate, which is sometimes quite difficult, especially for those who have really merged energetically and in some mysterious way have 'disappeared' into the exercise.

Nevertheless, I gently insist on separation. In my experience, it's difficult for people to remain aware and alert – sensitive to energy flow – for this length of time, without losing the thread, spacing out in thoughts and fantasies, or getting sexually turned on. It's also easy for one partner to get excited and override the other, galloping away with the energy in a direction that is too intimate or sexual.

Some people connect easily with the Circle of Light and the pleasure it brings. Men are often surprised by the sweetness and nourishing quality of the energy they receive from the woman's breasts, almost like a mother's milk, while women are sometimes delighted by their capacity to enjoy and receive male sexual energy without being penetrated physically.

Some people have difficulty, perhaps not being able to relax into a comfortable rhythm, or not being at ease with their partners. That's why I don't emphasize exact technique, why I tell people not to worry if they lose the rhythm. They'll find it again, in some way, and there is so much energy moving in the room that everyone is bound to be affected.

The exercise ends with the two partners sitting separately, eyes closed, absorbing and digesting the experience.

There is time for a second round and this time I ask my assistants to give everyone a blindfold to wear. When the blindfolds are on, I ask the women to slowly stand up, so that the assistants can gently guide them to a new, unknown male partner, where they slowly sit down in front of him.

Often in Tantra groups, people choose partners not based on energetic compatibility, but rather according to a certain stereotype, or image: somebody who is attractive to them, somebody good-looking, or young.... A man may have the idea that he likes a certain type of woman, but actually no energy is flowing between them – it's just an idea.

A 'blind date' situation gives people an opportunity to be with somebody they didn't choose, where they cannot use their normal criteria of judgment. It's an exciting experience, also a little scary, because you don't know who is with you.

We repeat the exercise, as before. My hope is, of course, that people will be pleasantly surprised by their capacity to enjoy somebody who is completely unknown, with whom they are interacting only through energy.

Finally, when the structure is finished and they're separated, I invite everyone to take off the blindfolds and see who they've been with. Usually, there are smiles and laughter, a recognition of shared intimacy.

Another option – also very interesting – is to move the partners to separate areas of the room before removing the blindfolds, so they never get to know with whom they did the Circle of Light.

It is also possible to create different circles between Tantric partners, using other polarities. For example, you can create a circle between the first and second chakras, but the risk here is that it will become too sexual because both chakras are located in the animal section of the body, in the instinctual area.

When a circle includes the heart there is always a shift of emphasis from down to up, from animal to divine – an upwardly rising quality that de-emphasizes a purely sexual and sensual meeting. And this, to me, is important, because Tantra spans the whole spectrum of human experience, a bridge between sex and super-consciousness.

By the end of the afternoon, it is clear that everyone has been touched by the experiment. Each participant will have had a slightly different experience, some more deeply pleasurable and ecstatic than others, but the fact that they have all allowed relative strangers to join with them in this kind of energy embrace is quite a radical thing.

Moreover, these lessons in sensitivity, intimacy and energy flow can all be taken home as keys, tips, to be used in more personal, intimate love relationships – something to explore with the beloved.

It may be thought that union with a member of the opposite sex in the Circle of Light brings the Tantric experience to a close, since most workshops of this kind tend to emphasize channeling sexual energy up through the body as the ultimate Tantric act.

But to me, Tantra is a much more multi-dimensional experience, more like a lifestyle than a sexual exploration, so the next stage of my Tantric Pulsation workshops is designed for something radically different and also quite unique – I will describe it in the last chapter.

Chapter Seventeen

The Tantric Lifestyle

"Surf's up!"

In the late 1950's, this familiar cry, uttered by leisure-oriented, thrill-seeking young men, ignited a sub-culture of music, movies, fashion and language as more and more people turned on to the fact that floating on a long piece of polished wood, a hundred yards offshore, and waiting for the right wave to carry you in, could produce a feeling of excitement and exhilaration unavailable on dry land.

The sheer joy, the outrageous buzz, of balancing on a narrow, speeding plank, using twists and turns of one's own body to guide the frail craft, while harnessing the power of a rolling, breaking wave, proved enormously appealing.

The art of surfing was not new. It developed in Hawaii, hundreds of years ago, and in 1779 Captain Cook's crew became the first white men to view the sport, marveling at the courage and skill of the native surfers. "The boldness with which we saw them perform these difficult and dangerous maneuvers, was altogether astonishing, and is scarcely to be credited," chronicled one of the English seamen, most of whom could not even swim.

A few decades later, in the 1820's, puritanical missionaries invaded the Hawaiian islands to 'civilize' the population and, true to type, viewed surfing as a hedonistic waste of time. Their disapproval nearly succeeded in making it extinct.

But a dedicated, irreverent club formed by island 'beach boys' popularized it again in the early 1900s and passed the torch to the mainland, infiltrating American culture and eventually spawning a new sound in music.

229

"Everybody's going surfing, surfing USA...," declared the Beach Boys pop group in the early 1960's and ever since then the image of surfing has been embedded in our culture – in the global culture, too.

Now millions of people around the world, most of whom never paddled a surfboard out to sea, spend hours every day sitting in front of their computers to 'surf the web,' switching from site to site, following one link to the next.

The imagery of the word 'surfing' suggests a delicate mix of personal initiative and surrender to forces beyond individual control: you choose the wave, but the energy of the wave is something you ride. You use the force to steer your course, but the power itself is not yours.

To me, surfing is a beautiful image to describe the Tantric lifestyle. We are part of a universal life force. We are riding waves on a vast and limitless ocean of energy. And if we awaken our own energy sources, falling in tune with the surrounding cosmic sea, we can surf through life, finding it as exciting and exhilarating as any beach boy shooting the Banzai Pipeline off Oahu's North Shore.

Reich, ever the ambitious scientist, set out to map this ocean of energy. His initial interest in the causes of human neurosis led him to investigate human sexuality, which in turn led him to probe the basic dynamics of life itself.

Life, he discovered, needs to pulsate. Energy needs to flow; if it cannot move, it stagnates. As far as the human organism is concerned, without a healthy, pulsating flow of energy, any idea of enjoying life and its pleasures will remain simply that – an idea, an empty concept, a fantasy.

Tantra also offers several maps based on energy flow, which is why the Reichian work is helpful as preparation, removing armoring that prevents energy from flowing through the body, especially around the belly and pelvic area.

Once energy is freed from blocks, once it has been awakened and released, then you can use it, celebrate and enjoy it. Then you can surf the waves of life, because you can feel where the energy wants to go and you know how to follow it.

When I talk in my workshops about Tantric maps, I begin by introducing Reich's map of energy moving between core and periphery, as explained in chapter two, and the hollow tube that facilitates this flow. As energy is 'breathed' in and out, along with the inhale and exhale, a strong pulsation is established, and a sense of wholeness is created by apparent opposites, embracing both the inner and outer worlds.

Another map I use in my Tantra work focuses on the human spine and its capacity as a vertical conductor of energy. Here, the flow is up and down, rather than in and out.

Energetically, the spine extends downwards, grounding us into the earth, while at the other end of the polarity it directs energy skyward. When energy flows up the spine, as in the Chakra Breathing exercise, we can easily get in touch with a sense of expansion and a taste of blissfulness.

This brings me to the map of the chakras and the Reichian muscle segments, because the spine is the crucial link between them all. As energy rises through the spine, vibrating the seven chakras as it flows upwards, we can experience the multi-dimensional nature of our existence: from animal, to human, to divine. We find out how it feels to meet someone from the third chakra, to dance from the second, to give and receive love from the fourth.

It is easy to get overwhelmed by the complexity of the chakras, which is why I keep things experience-based and non-intellectual. We don't spend a lot of time on theory in my workshops. I want people to use these maps as practical tools, as handy ways to read the weather and the waves and find out where the surf is rolling.

Another map, which I spoke about in chapter sixteen, is the basic movement of energy between polarities and this, in human terms, means the attraction between man and woman.

To give people a taste of male-female polarity in a simple and enjoyable way, I separate men and women and invite them to dance for each other.

I ask the women to form a large circle around the men, and tell the men to turn inwards, facing each other, their backs to the women. I play earthy, African drumming music and invite the men to dance together, giving each other support and building up a strong charge of male energy. It is primitive, animalistic, first chakra dancing.

When the men have connected with this feeling and their energy is high, I ask them to turn around and dance for the women. I encourage the women to appreciate this masculine quality and receive it.

Some women find this a little bit scary, but those who are in touch with their own inner masculine side can get excited and dance with the men in the same way, while others enjoy receiving the male energy in a feminine way.

As the drumming fades, I ask the men to form an outer circle and for the women to go inside, dancing with each other, not looking at men. Now I play music with a Middle Eastern, belly dance flavor, reflecting the quality of feminine energy: softer, smoother, silkier, perhaps a little more hidden, more sensual – more connected to the second chakra.

When they have embodied this energy and are supporting each other, I invite the women to turn around and dance with the men, playing seductively with their eyes, their hands, their bodies.

I encourage the men to allow themselves to be seduced by these attractive and mysterious women, now coming towards them, and to respond.

In this way, both men and women have the opportunity to experience what energy polarity really means. It is not merely an idea. It is a living, breathing reality, immediately affecting our lives and our relationships.

By the time we get to the Circle of Light, mentioned in the previous chapter, people are ready to bring all these principles and maps together. We're using breathing, the hollow tube, the image of core and periphery, to deepen energy flow. We use the chakra map and the spine to circle energy between the first and fourth energy centers, adding male-female polarity to bring two bodies together as one energy circuit.

Again, it's experience that counts. I want people to reclaim the natural energy that sustains us all as living beings, because it is this energy that can make life an ongoing dance and a celebration – a surfer's paradise.

As people become more sensitive to their own energy, more in tune with its impulses, I introduce a powerful exercise that offers a deep experience of 'surfing,' in the sense of inviting people to follow energy flow wherever it leads, at whatever risk.

The exercise, called 'Seven Spaces,' focuses on the polarities that we find in the second chakra: the issue of togetherness and aloneness, merging with other people and separating from them.

It is this energy center that tells us what we need, which impulse to follow, whether to move towards other people or away from them. The way we are designed, we need both. We need the nourishment and warmth of coming close, and we also need to move away, getting a bit of fresh air.

The mechanism of the belly center develops from the earliest connection of a child with its mother. A baby requires a state of merger with its mother almost all the time – in fact, in the womb, this merged state is continuous for nine months – but as it gets older and more independent the baby begins to move away and explore on its own, safe in knowing the maternal connection is still there and can be restored at any time.

As adults, the condition of being together or being separate, being merged or being alone, is a strong issue in love relationships. Many people have difficulties in finding the right balance and their dilemma can take on almost life-threatening proportions because it is tied so deeply to primal issues.

If the mother leaves, the baby will die, and these deep-seated feelings of survival panic can easily be triggered in co-dependent adults when a loved one walks out the door – if only for a night out with the boys.

Most people don't understand that the two conditions are equally important – that the condition of closeness and the condition of separateness are not opposites but complementaries, like two halves of one whole.

Instead, we try to choose one or the other, leaning toward dependency or anti-dependency. A dependent person wants to be close with the beloved because this feels safe and secure, and tries to deny or suppress the feeling when it's time to take a break.

An anti-dependent person chooses the opposite, preferring the security of being alone, without any emotional ties or attachments, and tries to suppress the longing for intimacy and love.

Either way, dynamic movement between the two polarities is lost and the energy of the second chakra becomes stuck – nothing can move when one pole is chosen against the other. When both poles are active, there can be a strong and healthy flow of energy between them.

My aim is to help people listen more carefully to their bellies, so they can hear the signals emanating from the second chakra and recognize when it's time to be together and when it's time to be alone.

As preparation, I take the group through a number of exercises designed to focus attention on the belly, using soft stress positions to awaken energy and bring more awareness to this area.

Then I send the participants on an extended break so my assistants can set up the room for 'Seven Spaces.' The pace is frantic because we have about 45 minutes to transform an ordinary group-room into a second chakra wonderland.

During this time, we create as many aspects, or tastes, of the belly center as we can, the most basic being a line down the middle of the room – conjured out of cushions – that divides a space of togetherness from a space of aloneness.

Dance and movement are essential qualities of the second chakra and I emphasize this by creating a big dance area in the middle of the room. Throughout the structure, I will be playing a range of music that invites many different kinds of body movement and expression through dancing.

When people move together, a lively play of energy happens through dancing: checking out attraction, gradually coming closer, flirting through the music, maybe becoming sensual....

The line separating the two basic spaces of togetherness and aloneness runs right through the middle of the dance area, enabling participants to move easily from one to the other, depending on how they feel.

Sometimes, a person can enjoy dancing so much – the movement, the sensations of the body as it responds to the music – that he, or she, doesn't have any desire to relate with others. The dance is so absorbing, it's enough to be by oneself.

On the togetherness side of the room, we create three more spaces, beginning with a 'hang out' area with lots of cushions and mattresses where people can lie, recline, or sit, with opportunities for friendly hugging and cuddling.

Another space is created for playing innocently together, like children. This area is based on a meditation technique developed by Osho called 'Born Again,' in which he encourages people to re-live their childhood, but this time enjoying all the things they were prevented from doing by their parents – being noisy, rolling around, grabbing pillows, teasing other children, having fun.

This is not a space for exploring childhood wounds. It is a play space, a sand box environment, allowing people to come close to others without being limited to grown-up activities like making conversation. It offers a way to be physically close without being sexual – tumbling around together, giggling or tickling each other.

This 'born again' space looks similar to the 'hang out' space, created with mattresses and cushions, but with a few added extras, such as balloons and teddy bears.

The fourth space on the togetherness side is a Tantra Temple, which we create by hanging long pieces of chiffon and silk from cords, using the colors pink, red, orange and purple.

Inside we put lots of mattresses, to make a soft floor, with red cushions shaped like hearts piled here and there. It's a place for people to go when they clearly feel sensual or sexual, when they have met someone special in other social areas and want to melt in a deep embrace.

Crossing the line into the aloneness space, we create a solo 'hang out' area, where a person can relax and be alone. Nearby, there is a 'Himalayan Cave,' an enclosed area created in the same way as the Tantra Temple, using cool colors like green and blue, furnished only with meditation cushions. Here, people can sit silently and meditate in a space of deep aloneness, removed from the rest of the world.

235

Emotions are part of the belly center and people often feel anger or tears welling up, triggered either by togetherness or aloneness. For them, a special 'gibberish corner' is created: a small room heavily padded with mattresses with a big, thick curtain across the entrance, where people can go to scream, yell and weep. It's a great place to let off steam.

When the room is ready and everyone has returned from their break, I introduce the structure, saying that for the next two hours participants are not to use any words in their communication with each other – no talking at any time – but are otherwise free to use whatever sounds they like.

They are invited, each moment, to listen to the belly, listen to their own needs, their wants, and discover where in the room those needs can best be met. It's really a feeling of being pulled by the belly, from here to there, without restraint or calculation.

My emphasis is not on any particular experience, nor on arriving at any fixed idea about 'what kind of person I am.'

Energy is always moving. It is a flux, so the emphasis is on continuously referring to the belly, listening to its impulses and asking, "What do I want now? Do I want to be with this person? Do I want to be elsewhere? Is the energy changing? Does this feel good?"

The exercise offers tremendous freedom, because it gives people permission to be completely spontaneous and self-oriented, doing things they would never consider in normal social interaction.

For example, you're dancing with somebody, or lying together in the social hang-out space, and suddenly you get a feeling, "I don't want to be here. It's time to leave."

In normal society all kinds of difficulties present themselves when such feelings arise: How do I tell this person? How can I leave my boss, boyfriend, or brother, in the middle of a cocktail party? What will he think of me? What will the emotional fall-out be afterwards?

More often than not, a belly impulse of this kind has to be suppressed for the sake of harmony. But here, no social restrictions apply. Here, freedom of choice, moment to moment, is the only rule.

I am not presenting the 'Seven Spaces' as a permanent solution to social inhibition. I'm not suggesting we should behave like this all the time, in any situation. But in my experience our habits are so strong – overriding the energy of the second chakra in favor of politeness, protocol, morality – that we need a big explosion to throw away all the 'shoulds' and discover how to listen to our real needs.

Having made sure that everyone understands the exercise, I start playing music and invite everyone to begin.

Immediately, many people head for the 'born again' space to play, feeling intuitively that this is a good way to get energy moving, relax and become familiar with being spontaneous.

Others head for the social hang out area, sitting or lying down, getting cozy with someone they know. Still others start dancing to the infectious trance beat of the music.

Men, for some reason, seem more interested than women in being alone in the early stages of the exercise, and four or five of them move across the line to be by themselves.

The Tantra Temple is empty and will probably stay that way for quite a while. Although the idea of an intimate physical meeting is attractive, it also tends to be scary. The idea of sexual intimacy seems appealing, but the belly may be asking for something more light and playful.

Often, our constant preoccupation with sex comes more from the mind than from a true energetic source. When people listen to the second chakra, they often realize they want to dance, play, or cuddle.

But neither will the temple stay empty for two hours. It takes time for people to get warmed up and then a few couples will explore this aspect of their energy.

For much of the exercise I am focused on the music, tuning into the general atmosphere of the group and supporting it with the right pace and rhythm.

It's a pity that the practical necessity of creating all seven spaces in one room allows only one kind of music to be played at a time, because this is bound to influence people's moods, whereas my first choice would be to have different music for all seven spaces – including absolute silence in the Himalayan cave.

I keep the energy alive and moving with dance music as the dominant theme, sometimes weaving in quiet, meditative melodies to suit the overall mood.

The rest of the time, I am observing the participants, watching the flow of movement around the room, seeing the dynamics that bring people together and send them apart.

For example, one young woman in her early twenties develops a pattern of dancing in the social section, attracting attention from several men, then moving across the line into the space of dancing alone.

I can see this is her way of keeping her own center, not getting too lost in the game of flirting and connecting, playing the social game the way she wants, not allowing anyone to invade her privacy.

A German man, aged about 35, spends a lot of time and energy in the social areas, then slowly is drawn to spending more and more time in the alone half of the room.

Afterwards, he tells me that he came into the group with sex on his mind, but what he actually discovered was a strong desire to spend more time by himself. He thought he was a just party animal, when underneath he was really longing for some quality meditation time.

I also see people going into the alone 'hang-out' space to sulk. Unquestionably, this is one aspect of being alone, but it also touches my heart because a few of them look back at the social scene with such longing in their eyes, wanting to connect, too overwhelmed by some old feeling of paralysis or social ineptitude.

Maybe someone tried to connect with a member of the opposite sex and got ignored or rejected, and has retired here to lick his or her wounds.

Rejection is never comfortable or welcome, but it can be a valuable experience, because this is an artificial situation and the impact of being rejected is not as great as in day-to-day life. It's not like you're living in Anchorage, in the middle of an Arctic winter, and the only woman you know in the whole of Alaska has just said 'no' to you.

Here, people have more distance and can ask themselves, "Well, was my belly really pulling me towards that woman, or was the impulse coming from my mind, from my habitual ideas about who I find attractive?"

Every incident that happens during these two hours is an opportunity to explore, to experiment in a safe environment. It's a kind of play or drama, with many characters with whom to interact.

There are amusing moments. One man who has spent most of the morning in the Himalayan cave, suddenly bursts out through the drapes, runs across the room and dives into the 'gibberish corner,' yelling and screaming. Then, after a few minutes, he runs across the line to the togetherness area and dances enthusiastically, connecting with several women.

There are no long term consequences, so people feel free to explore without hesitation or calculation. It gives them a chance to meet lightly, to meet intensely, to try new things, initiate, risk rejection, gain acceptance, bypass the mind, listen to energy and free up the capacity for spontaneity which is so blocked in most of us.

The mind can, of course, get very active in this structure and judge each situation – "What are you doing here in the born again space, laughing and playing like a child? You've just been rejected, you should be alone and miserable" – but in this free-flowing situation things are changing so fast that people don't have time to dwell on specific incidents.

Watching the dynamics of 'Seven Spaces,' I can see all of these experiences happening to individual participants, and I also see the collective organism they are creating through their movements.

As the exercise deepens and the energy in the room intensifies, they are all somehow engulfed by the oceanic quality of the second chakra. Even though they are focused on themselves, on their immediate needs, they are creating a harmonious dance, like separate fronds of a large bed of seaweed, washed by eddies of the tides, dancing under the sea.

239

People move around the different spaces, following the impulses of their bellies, going here and there, immersed in this watery feeling of ebb and flow. As I see it, it's a reflection of the cosmic ocean. Their efforts may be awkward at times, but these people are, unquestionably, learning how to surf the waves of energy that come rolling through the room.

Some are graceful in the way they move, in tune with the waves, while others fall off their boards and get wiped out. But the damage is temporary and soon they are climbing back on their surfboards, waiting for the next wave.

Two hours fly by quickly and, at the end of Seven Spaces, I invite people to express whatever has been most important for them in terms of self-understanding.

Responses vary widely. Some people, like the man I mentioned earlier, realize they have been spending too much time in routine socializing, when in reality they want to spend more time by themselves. For others, the reverse is true: they have been isolating themselves out of fear and now they want to enjoy more human contact.

Many say they feel more alive and bubbly, more in touch with their energy, while at the same time more relaxed and centered in themselves.

Listening to the participants, I have a trusting attitude that people get what they need, what is right for them, what they are capable of receiving at this moment in their journey of self-exploration.

For my part, I never feel that people miss the point, because each workshop contains so many different experiences that something always happens for everyone...some energy moves, some insight deepens.

If people are intelligent they will continue to nourish these new developments, not allowing old habits to creep back in and deaden the new flame of aliveness that is flickering inside.

Fundamentally, my work is about saying 'yes' to life. This, in turn, means saying 'yes' to energy, and this is why I value Osho, Reich and Tantra so much. Their methods help us celebrate the art of being alive.

When our energy is streaming and flowing within us, pulsating with the same rhythm as the universe that surrounds us, we immediately feel at home in ourselves, in tune with nature, at one with existence.

We are happy and grateful for the experience of being alive.

Aneesha L. Dillon was born in the USA in 1949 on the New Jersey coast, south of New York City, and grew up in suburban NJ, Ohio, and Pennsylvania.

She received her bachelor's degree in Philosophy and Political Science from Boston University, then moved to California for new adventures.

Her fascination with Humanistic Psychology and particularly the writings of Wilhelm Reich led her to train in neo-Reichian breathing and body work at Charles Kelley's Radix Institute where, after 2 ½ years she graduated as the Institute's first Certified Radix Teacher.

After two years living and leading groups at Esalen Institute, Big Sur California, Aneesha traveled to India in 1976 to learn the revolutionary active meditation techniques of Osho (then, Bhagwan Rajneesh). He invited her to lead neo-Reichian groups in his ashram in Pune, as part of his unique program combining Western psychotherapy methods with Eastern techniques of meditation.

For nearly 30 years Aneesha has lived and worked in Osho centers and communes worldwide, developing her work, 'Pulsation', a meeting of neo-Reichian bodywork, breathing, and emotional release with meditation.

During the last 10 years, she has created Tantric Pulsation, which explores the razor's edge of sexuality, sensitivity and blissfulness, where sexual energy can be transformed into meditation.

For further information about Aneesha's groups and trainings in Pulsation and Tantric Pulsation: www.oshopulsation.com

Printed in the United States
53485LVS00002B/233